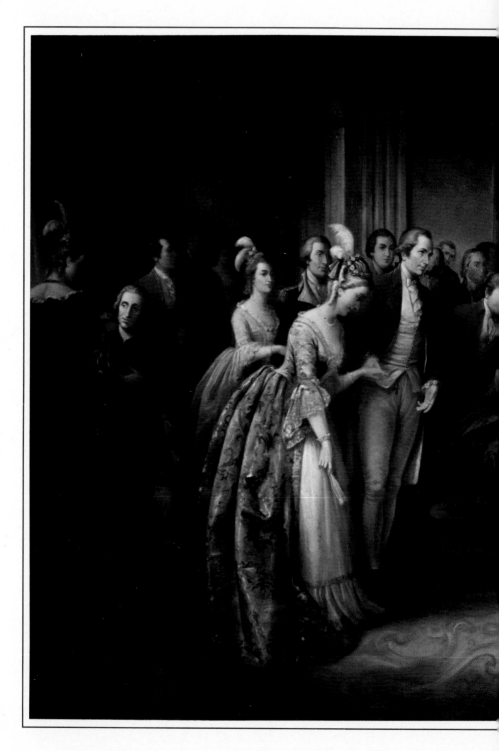

Published by the WHITE HOUSE HISTORICAL ASSOCIATION
With the Cooperation of the NATIONAL GEOGRAPHIC SOCIETY, Washington, D. C.

The First Ladies

By Margaret Brown Klapthor

THE FIRST LADIES

By *Margaret Brown Klapthor*, Chairman,
    Department of National and Military History,
    National Museum of History and Technology,
    Smithsonian Institution

PRODUCED BY THE NATIONAL GEOGRAPHIC SOCIETY
    AS A PUBLIC SERVICE
Melvin M. Payne, Chairman of the Board
Robert E. Doyle, President
Gilbert M. Grosvenor, Editor
Melville Bell Grosvenor, Editor Emeritus

PREPARED BY THE SPECIAL PUBLICATIONS DIVISION
Robert L. Breeden, Editor
Donald J. Crump, Associate Editor
Philip B. Silcott, Senior Editor
Mary Ann Harrell, Managing Editor
Susan C. Burns, Jennifer Urquhart, Research
Geraldine Linder, Picture Editor
*Marie Bradby, Louis de la Haba, P. Tyrus Harrington,
    Margaret McKelway*, Captions
Ursula Perrin Vosseler, Art Director
Robert W. Messer, Production Manager; *George
    V. White*, Assistant Production Manager;
    *June L. Graham, Raja D. Murshed, Christine A.
    Roberts, David V. Showers*, Production
    Assistants
John R. Metcalfe, Engraving and Printing
*Joseph H. Bailey, Sean Baldwin, J. Bruce Baumann,
    Victor R. Boswell, Jr., David S. Boyer, Nelson H.
    Brown, Dan J. Dry, Thomas Hooper, Larry
    Kinney, Bates Littlehales, George F. Mobley,
    Robert S. Oakes, Martin Rogers, James E.
    Russell, Joseph J. Scherschel, Volkmar Wentzel*,
    Photography
STAFF FOR SECOND EDITION: *Bonnie S. Lawrence*,
    Research; *Jane H. Buxton*, Project
    Coordinator; *Suez B. Kehl, Cinda Rose*, Design,
    Turner Houston, Assistant; *Debra A. Antonini,
    Barbara Bricks, Rosamund Garner, Suzanne J.
    Jacobson, Cleo Petroff, Katheryn M. Slocum,
    Suzanne Venino*, Staff Assistants

White House staff members who assisted during the preparation of this edition: *Mary Finch Hoyt*, Press Secretary to Mrs. Carter; *Faith Collins, Vikki Lovett*, Press Office; *Billie B. Shaddix*, Director of Photographic Services; *Betty Monkman*, Registrar

Visitors' view of the Executive Mansion in winter—a steel engraving—illustrated a noteworthy venture in biography: Laura C. Holloway's The Ladies of the White House, *first published in 1870 and apparently the first book on First Ladies.*

COVER: *Portrait of Martha Washington, painted by E. F. Andrews in 1878, hangs in the East Room of the White House as a companion piece for the Gilbert Stuart portrait of her husband.*
OVERLEAF: *George and Martha Washington appear at right in an unknown artist's "Reception at Mount Vernon." Its style suggests a fictionalized illustration for a 19th-century popular magazine. Previously unpublished, the painting hangs in the headquarters of the National Society of the Daughters of the American Revolution, Washington, D. C., on loan from the Rhode Island Society.*

Foreword

Being the wife of the President of the United States has always brought opportunities for service as well as glamour and privilege. But the opportunities and services have been as varied through the years as have the times and personalities of the women who assumed that distinctive role.

This book, first published in 1975 and now in its second edition, presents thumbnail sketches of the Presidents' wives and other ladies who presided in turn over the Executive Mansion. Some were daughters or other relatives of Presidents who came as widowers, or with wives in poor health. James Buchanan, our only bachelor President, was fortunate in having his lovely niece, Harriet Lane, to act as his official hostess with charm and discretion in the face of secession and imminent civil war.

In reading these brief biographies, I was struck by the number of "Women Doers"—to use the term chosen by Lady Bird Johnson (herself a notable doer) to describe active and successful American women.

Martha Washington never lived in the Executive Mansion of the city named for the first President. Yet she left an indelible dignity to the position of "First Lady"—a title that became current in the 1880's, after a reporter applied it to Frances Folsom as the bride of Grover Cleveland.

We remember Martha Washington as a devoted wife and a gracious hostess in the temporary capitals of New York and Philadelphia. Less well known is the fact that during the Revolution she traveled each year over long, hazardous roads to join the General in winter camp with his troops.

Abigail Adams, the first First Lady to live in the newly built White House, also supported the Revolution, and managed the family farm alone while John Adams advocated "independency" at the Continental Congress. Later, at his side, she showed her political wisdom and wit to such effect that opponents chided her as "Mrs. President." Shrewd and capable Sarah Polk acted as a private secretary to President Polk, who trusted her judgment in everything. Edith Wilson protected her sick husband so diligently that she, too, was called "Mrs. President."

Though wives of early Presidents shunned politics in public, many helped in their own way: Dolley Madison's personal popularity gave noteworthy support to her husband's crisis-torn regime. Not until Eleanor Roosevelt, however, did a First Lady figure in the mainstream of politics and social issues—thus inspiring women everywhere to seek more respect and influence through careers in or out of government.

President Carter and I congratulate Margaret Brown Klapthor as the author of this lively and informative book, and we are deeply grateful to the National Geographic Society and the White House Historical Association for their cooperation in producing and publishing it.

Rosalynn Carter

"Lincoln's Last Reception," a lithograph hastily published after his assassination, portrays him and Mrs. Lincoln among heroes of the Union cause on the night of his second inauguration, March 4, 1865. The artist places Vice President Andrew Johnson, who was ill, at Lincoln's side as he greets Mrs. Ulysses S. Grant, although neither she nor the general attended.

Contents

Martha Dandridge Custis Washington
1731-1802

"I think I am more like a state prisoner than anything else, there is certain bounds set for me which I must not depart from. . . ." So in one of her few surviving letters, Martha Washington confided to a niece that she did not entirely enjoy her role as first of First Ladies. She once conceded that "many younger and gayer women would be extremely pleased" in her place; she would "much rather be at home."

But when George Washington took his oath of office in New York City on April 30, 1789, and assumed the new duties of President of the United States, his wife brought to their position a tact and discretion developed over 58 years of life in Tidewater Virginia society.

Oldest daughter of John and Frances Dandridge, she was born June 2, 1731, on a plantation near Williamsburg. Typical for a girl in an 18th-century family, her education was almost negligible except in domestic and social skills, but she learned all the arts of a well-ordered household and how to keep a family contented.

As a girl of 18 — about five feet tall, dark-haired, gentle of manner — she married the wealthy Daniel Parke Custis. Two babies died; two were hardly past infancy when her husband died in 1757.

From the day Martha married George Washington in 1759, her great concern was the comfort and happiness of her husband and her children. When his career led him to the battlegrounds of the Revolutionary War and finally to the Presidency, she followed him bravely. Her love of private life equaled her husband's; but, as she wrote to her friend Mercy Otis Warren, "I cannot blame him for having acted according to his ideas of duty in obeying the voice of his country." As for herself, "I am still determined to be cheerful and to be happy, in whatever situation I may be; for I have also learned from experience that the greater part of our happiness or misery depends upon our dispositions, and not upon our circumstances."

At the President's House in temporary capitals, New York and Philadelphia, the Washingtons chose to entertain in formal style, deliberately emphasizing the new republic's wish to be accepted as the equal of the established governments of Europe. Still, Martha's warm hospitality made her guests feel welcome and put strangers at ease. She took little satisfaction in "formal compliments and empty ceremonies," and declared that "I am fond only of what comes from the heart." Abigail Adams, who sat at her right during parties and receptions, praised her as "one of those unassuming characters which create Love & Esteem."

In 1797 the Washingtons said farewell to public life and returned to their beloved Mount Vernon, to live surrounded by kinfolk, friends, and a constant stream of guests eager to pay their respects to the celebrated couple. Martha's daughter Patsy had died at 17, her son Jack at 26, but Jack's children figured in the household. After George Washington died in 1799, Martha assured a final·privacy by burning their letters; she died of a "severe fever" on May 22, 1802. Both lie buried at Mount Vernon, where Washington himself had planned an unpretentious tomb for them.

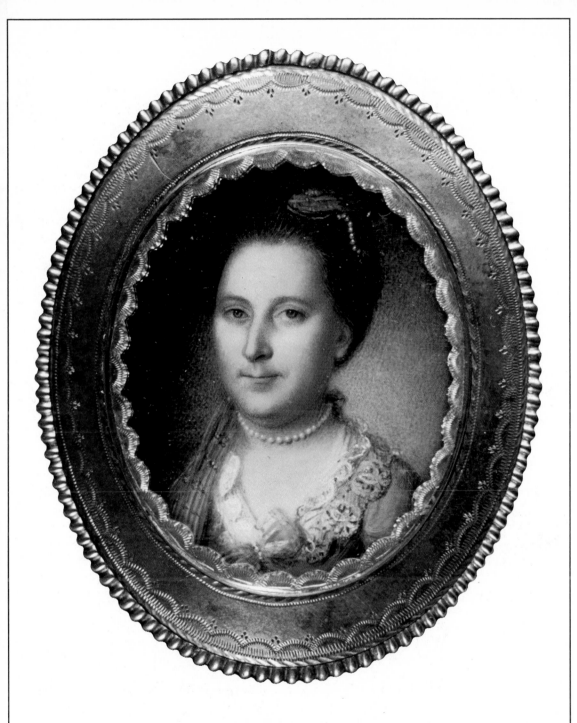

"Dear Patsy" to her husband, Martha Washington had this miniature painted by Charles Willson Peale about 1776; through the rest of the Revolutionary War, the general wore it in a gold locket. "Lady Washington," some admiring Americans called her; in a modest reference to her domestic skill, she described herself as an "old-fashioned Virginia house-keeper." "A most becoming pleasentness sits upon her countanance...," wrote Abigail Adams in 1789.

Abigail Smith Adams
1744-1818

Inheriting New England's strongest traditions, Abigail Smith was born in 1744 at Weymouth, Massachusetts. On her mother's side she was descended from the Quincys, a family of great prestige in the colony; her father and other forebears were Congregational ministers, leaders in a society that held its clergy in high esteem.

Like other women of the time, Abigail lacked formal education; but her curiosity spurred her keen intelligence, and she read avidly the books at hand. Reading created a bond between her and young John Adams, Harvard graduate launched on a career in law, and they were married in 1764. It was a marriage of the mind and of the heart, enduring for more than half a century, enriched by time.

The young couple lived on John's small farm at Braintree or in Boston as his practice expanded. In ten years she bore three sons and two daughters; she looked after family and home when he went traveling as circuit judge. "Alass!" she wrote in December 1773, "How many snow banks devide thee and me...."

Long separations kept Abigail from her husband while he served the country they loved, as delegate to the Continental Congress, envoy abroad, elected officer under the Constitution. Her letters—pungent, witty, and vivid, spelled just as she spoke—detail her life in times of revolution. They tell the story of the woman who stayed at home to struggle with wartime shortages and inflation; to run the farm with a minimum of help; to teach four children when formal education was interrupted. Most of all, they tell of her loneliness without her "dearest Friend." That "one single expression," she said, "dwelt upon my mind and playd about my Heart...."

In 1784, she joined him at his diplomatic post in Paris, and observed with interest the manners of the French. After 1785, she filled the difficult role of wife of the first United States Minister to Great Britain, and did so with dignity and tact. They returned happily in 1788 to Massachusetts and the handsome house they had just acquired in Braintree, later called Quincy, home for the rest of their lives.

As wife of the first Vice President, Abigail became a good friend to Mrs. Washington and a valued help in official entertaining, drawing on her experience of courts and society abroad. After 1791, however, poor health forced her to spend as much time as possible in Quincy. Illness or trouble found her resolute; as she once declared, she would "not forget the blessings which sweeten life."

When John Adams was elected President, she continued a formal pattern of entertaining—even in the primitive conditions she found at the new capital in November 1800. The city was wilderness, the President's House far from completion. Her private complaints to her family provide blunt accounts of both, but for her three months in Washington she duly held her dinners and receptions.

The Adamses retired to Quincy in 1801, and for 17 years enjoyed the companionship that public life had long denied them. Abigail died in 1818, and is buried beside her husband in United First Parish Church. She leaves her country a most remarkable record as patriot and First Lady, wife of one President and mother of another.

Proudly appearing in London as a citizen of her newly independent country, wife of its first diplomat to the court of King George III, Abigail Adams sat in 1785 for her portrait by a young American artist and family friend, Mather Brown. Some scholars identify the painting above as Brown's, which passed out of family hands; others attribute it to Ralph Earl, another artist from Massachusetts who spent part of 1785 in London. It came to light in the 1930's as "Portrait of a Lady." Well-authenticated portraits by other painters confirm the likeness to Abigail Adams at about the age of 40.

Jefferson's daughter Martha ("Patsy") posed for this oil-on-ivory miniature in 1789, at age 17; "a delicate likeness of her father," a friend called her during the White House years when she sometimes served as his hostess. Of her mother, whose name she bore, no portrait of any kind has survived.

Martha Wayles Skelton Jefferson
1748-1782

When Thomas Jefferson came courting, Martha Wayles Skelton at 22 was already a widow, an heiress, and a mother whose firstborn son would die in early childhood. Family tradition says that she was accomplished and beautiful—with slender figure, hazel eyes, and auburn hair—and wooed by many. Perhaps a mutual love of music cemented the romance; Jefferson played the violin, and one of the furnishings he ordered for the home he was building at Monticello was a "forte-piano" for his bride.

They were married on New Year's Day, 1772, at the bride's plantation home "The Forest," near Williamsburg. When they finally reached Monticello in a late January snowstorm to find no fire, no food, and the servants asleep, they toasted their new home with a leftover half-bottle of wine and "song and merriment and laughter." That night, on their own mountaintop, the love of Thomas Jefferson and his bride seemed strong enough to endure any adversity.

The birth of their daughter Martha in September increased their happiness. Within ten years the family gained five more children. Of them all, only two lived to grow up: Martha, called Patsy, and Mary, called Maria or Polly.

The physical strain of frequent pregnancies weakened Martha Jefferson so gravely that her husband curtailed his political activities to stay near her. He served in Virginia's House of Delegates and as governor, but he refused an appointment by the Continental Congress as a commissioner to France. Just after New Year's Day, 1781, a British invasion forced Martha to flee the capital in Richmond with a baby girl a few weeks old—who died in April. In June the family barely escaped an enemy raid on Monticello. She bore another daughter the following May, and never regained a fair measure of strength. Jefferson wrote on May 20 that her condition was dangerous. After months of tending her devotedly, he noted in his account book for September 6, "My dear wife died this day at 11-45 A.M."

Apparently he never brought himself to record their life together; in a memoir he referred to ten years "in unchequered happiness." Half a century later his daughter Martha remembered his sorrow: "the violence of his emotion . . . to this day I dare not describe to myself." For three weeks he had shut himself in his room, pacing back and forth until exhausted. Slowly that first anguish spent itself. In November he agreed to serve as commissioner to France, eventually taking "Patsy" with him in 1784 and sending for "Polly" later.

When Jefferson became President in 1801, he had been a widower for 19 years. He had become as capable of handling social affairs as political matters. Occasionally he called on Dolley Madison for assistance. And it was Patsy—now Mrs. Thomas Mann Randolph, Jr.—who appeared as the lady of the President's House in the winter of 1802-1803, when she spent seven weeks there. She was there again in 1805-1806, and gave birth to a son named for James Madison, the first child born in the White House. It was Martha Randolph with her family who shared Jefferson's retirement at Monticello until he died there in 1826.

Dolley Payne Todd Madison
1768-1849

For half a century she was the most important woman in the social circles of America. To this day she remains one of the best-known and best loved ladies of the White House—though often referred to, mistakenly, as Dorothy or Dorothea.

She always called herself Dolley; and by that name the New Garden Monthly Meeting of the Society of Friends, in piedmont North Carolina, recorded her birth to John and Mary Coles Payne, settlers from Virginia. In 1769 John Payne took his family back to his home colony, and in 1783 he moved them to Philadelphia, city of the Quakers. Dolley grew up in the strict discipline of the Society, but nothing muted her happy personality and her warm heart.

John Todd, Jr., a lawyer, exchanged marriage vows with Dolley in 1790. Just three years later he died in a yellow-fever epidemic, leaving his wife with a small son.

By this time Philadelphia had become the capital city. With her charm and her laughing blue eyes, fair skin, and black curls, the young widow attracted distinguished attention. Before long Dolley was reporting to her best friend that "the great little Madison has asked. . . . to see me this evening."

Although Representative James Madison of Virginia was 17 years her senior, and Episcopalian in background, they were married in September 1794. The marriage, though childless, was notably happy; "our hearts understand each other," she assured him. He could even be patient with Dolley's son, Payne, who mishandled his own affairs—and, eventually, mismanaged Madison's estate.

Discarding the somber Quaker dress after her second marriage, Dolley chose the finest of fashions. Margaret Bayard Smith, chronicler of early Washington social life, wrote: "She looked a Queen. . . . It would be *absolutely impossible* for any one to behave with more perfect propriety than she did."

Blessed with a desire to please and a willingness to be pleased, Dolley made her home the center of society when Madison began, in 1801, his eight years as Jefferson's Secretary of State. She assisted at the White House when the President asked her help in receiving ladies, and presided at the first inaugural ball in Washington when her husband became Chief Executive in 1809.

Dolley's social graces made her famous. Her political acumen, prized by her husband, is less renowned, though her gracious tact smoothed many a quarrel. Hostile statesmen, difficult envoys from Spain or Tunisia, warrior chiefs from the west, flustered youngsters—she always welcomed everyone. Forced to flee from the White House by a British army during the War of 1812, she returned to find the mansion in ruins. Undaunted by temporary quarters, she entertained as skillfully as ever.

At their plantation Montpelier in Virginia, the Madisons lived in pleasant retirement until he died in 1836. She returned to the capital in the autumn of 1837, and friends found tactful ways to supplement her diminished income. She remained in Washington until her death in 1849, honored and loved by all. The delightful personality of this unusual woman is a cherished part of her country's history.

Already a hostess of outstanding success, Dolley Madison sat for this portrait by Gilbert Stuart in 1804. As wife of the Secretary of State, she began her long career of official hospitality; she sustained it for eight years as First Lady. Her manners, said a contemporary, "would disarm envy itself." Widowed, impoverished, and old, she never lost her charm or dignity; she enjoyed the deepening respect of her friends and country to the last.

Invariably elegant, Elizabeth Monroe chose an ermine scarf to complement black velvet in Empire style for this portrait attributed to Benjamin West. Although she had gone abroad with her husband on diplomatic missions, delicate health limited her activities—and enjoyment—in her eight years as First Lady.

Elizabeth Kortright Monroe
1768-1830

Romance glints from the little that is known of Elizabeth Kortright's early life. She was born in New York City in 1768, daughter of an old New York family. Her father, Lawrence, had served the Crown by privateering during the French and Indian War and made a fortune. He took no active part in the War of Independence; and James Monroe wrote to his friend Thomas Jefferson in Paris in 1786 that he had married the daughter of a gentleman "injured in his fortunes" by the Revolution.

Strange choice, perhaps, for a patriot veteran with political ambitions and little money of his own; but Elizabeth was beautiful, and love was decisive. They were married in February 1786, when the bride was not yet 18.

The young couple planned to live in Fredericksburg, Virginia, where Monroe began his practice of law. His political career, however, kept them on the move as the family increased by two daughters and a son who died in infancy.

In 1794, Elizabeth Monroe accompanied her husband to France when President Washington appointed him United States Minister. Arriving in Paris in the midst of the French Revolution, she took a dramatic part in saving Lafayette's wife, imprisoned and expecting death on the guillotine. With only her servants in her carriage, the American Minister's wife went to the prison and asked to see Madame Lafayette. Soon after this hint of American interest, the prisoner was set free. The Monroes became very popular in France, where the diplomat's lady received the affectionate name of *la belle Américaine*.

For 17 years Monroe, his wife at his side, alternated between foreign missions and service as governor or legislator of Virginia. They made the plantation of Oak Hill their home after he inherited it from an uncle, and appeared on the Washington scene in 1811 when he became Madison's Secretary of State.

Elizabeth Monroe was an accomplished hostess when her husband took the Presidential oath in 1817. Through much of the administration, however, she was in poor health and curtailed her activities. Wives of the diplomatic corps and other dignitaries took it amiss when she decided to pay no calls — an arduous social duty in a city of widely scattered dwellings and unpaved streets.

Moreover, she and her daughter Eliza changed White House customs to create the formal atmosphere of European courts. Even the White House wedding of her daughter Maria was private, in "the New York style" rather than the expansive Virginia social style made popular by Dolley Madison. A guest at the Monroes' last levee, on New Year's Day in 1825, described the First Lady as "regal-looking" and noted details of interest: "Her dress was superb black velvet; neck and arms bare and beautifully formed; her hair in puffs and dressed high on the head and ornamented with white ostrich plumes; around her neck an elegant pearl necklace. Though no longer young, she is still a very handsome woman."

In retirement at Oak Hill, Elizabeth Monroe died on September 23, 1830; and family tradition says that her husband burned the letters of their life together.

Louisa Catherine Johnson Adams
1775-1852

Only First Lady born outside the United States, Louisa Catherine Adams did not come to this country until four years after she had married John Quincy Adams. Political enemies sometimes called her English. She was born in London to an English mother, Catherine Nuth Johnson, but her father was American—Joshua Johnson, of Maryland—and he served as United States consul after 1790.

A career diplomat at 27, accredited to the Netherlands, John Quincy developed his interest in charming 19-year-old Louisa when they met in London in 1794. Three years later they were married, and went to Berlin in course of duty. At the Prussian court she displayed the style and grace of a diplomat's lady; the ways of a Yankee farm community seemed strange indeed in 1801 when she first reached the country of which she was a citizen. Then began years divided among the family home in Quincy, Massachusetts, their house in Boston, and a political home in Washington, D. C. Now the Johnsons had settled in the capital, and Louisa always felt more at home there than she ever did in New England.

She left her two older sons in Massachusetts for education in 1809 when she took two-year-old Charles Francis to Russia, where Adams served as Minister. Despite the glamour of the tsar's court, she had to struggle with cold winters, strange customs, limited funds, and poor health; an infant daughter born in 1811 died the next year. Peace negotiations called Adams to Ghent in 1814 and then to London. To join him, Louisa had to make a forty-day journey across war-ravaged Europe by coach in winter; roving bands of stragglers and highwaymen filled her with "unspeakable terrors" for her son. Happily, the next two years gave her an interlude of family life in the country of her birth.

Appointment of John Quincy as Monroe's Secretary of State brought the Adamses to Washington in 1817, and Louisa's drawing room became a center for the diplomatic corps and other notables. Good music enhanced her Tuesday evenings at home, and theater parties contributed to her reputation as an outstanding hostess.

But the pleasure of moving to the White House in 1825 was dimmed by the bitter politics of the election and by her own poor health. She suffered from deep depression. Though she continued her weekly "drawing rooms," she preferred quiet evenings—reading, composing music and verse, playing her harp. The necessary entertainments were always elegant, however; and her cordial hospitality made the last official reception a gracious occasion although her husband had lost his bid for reelection and partisan feeling still ran high.

Louisa thought she was retiring to Massachusetts permanently, but in 1831 her husband began 17 years of notable service in the House of Representatives. The Adamses could look back on a secure happiness as well as many trials when they celebrated their fiftieth wedding anniversary at Quincy in 1847. He was fatally stricken at the Capitol the following year; she died in Washington in 1852, and today lies buried at his side in the family church at Quincy.

"Try as she might, the Madam could never be Bostonian, and it was her cross in life," wrote Henry Adams of his London-born grandmother. Nor did Louisa Johnson Adams feel at ease in what she called the "Bull Bait" of Washington's political life. Gilbert Stuart painted her portrait in 1821.

With the devotion that always marked their marriage, Andrew Jackson once assured Rachel: "recollection never fails me of your likeness." Nearly heartbroken by her death, he wore a miniature of her daily and kept it on his bedside table every night. Family tradition held that the portrait above was the very memento he carried, and attributed it to Anna C. Peale. Current scholarship identifies it as the work of Louisa Catherine Strobel, who was in France from 1815 to 1830; she probably copied a study from life, for one of "Aunt Rachel's" relatives.

Rachel Donelson Jackson
1767-1828

Wearing the white dress she had purchased for her husband's inaugural ceremonies in March 1829, Rachel Donelson Jackson was buried in the garden at The Hermitage, her home near Nashville, Tennessee, on Christmas Eve in 1828. Lines from her epitaph —"A being so gentle and so virtuous slander might wound, but could not dishonor" —reflected his bitterness at campaign slurs that seemed to precipitate her death.

Rachel Donelson was a child of the frontier. Born in Virginia, she journeyed to the Tennessee wilderness with her parents when only 12. At 17, while living in Kentucky, she married Lewis Robards, of a prominent Mercer County family. His unreasoning jealousy made it impossible for her to live with him; in 1790 they separated, and she heard that he was filing a petition for divorce.

Andrew Jackson married her in 1791; and after two happy years they learned to their dismay that Robards had not obtained a divorce, only permission to file for one. Now he brought suit on grounds of adultery. After the divorce was granted, the Jacksons quietly remarried in 1794. They had made an honest mistake, as friends well understood, but whispers of adultery and bigamy followed Rachel as Jackson's career advanced in both politics and war. He was quick to take offense at, and ready to avenge, any slight to her.

Scandal aside, Rachel's unpretentious kindness won the respect of all who knew her—including innumerable visitors who found a comfortable welcome at The Hermitage. Although the Jacksons never had children of their own, they gladly opened their home to the children of Rachel's many relatives. In 1809 they adopted a nephew and named him Andrew Jackson, Jr. They also reared other nephews; one, Andrew Jackson Donelson, eventually married his cousin Emily, one of Rachel's favorite nieces.

Jackson's hostess Emily Donelson: by his friend and portraitist Ralph E. W. Earl.

When Jackson was elected President, he planned to have young Donelson for private secretary, with Emily as company for Rachel. After losing his beloved wife he asked Emily to serve as his hostess.

Though only 21 when she entered the White House, she skillfully cared for her uncle, her husband, four children (three born at the mansion), many visiting relatives, and official guests. Praised by contemporaries for her wonderful tact, she had the courage to differ with the President on issues of principle. Frail throughout her lifetime, Emily died of tuberculosis in 1836.

During the last months of the administration, Sarah Yorke Jackson, wife of Andrew Jackson, Jr., presided at the mansion in her stead.

Hannah Hoes Van Buren
1783-1819

Cousins in a close-knit Dutch community, Hannah Hoes and Martin Van Buren grew up together in Kinderhook, New York. Evidently he wanted to establish his law practice before marrying his sweetheart — they were not wed until 1807, when he was 24 and his bride just three months younger. Apparently their marriage was a happy one, though little is known of Hannah as a person.

Van Buren omitted even her name from his autobiography; a gentleman of that day would not shame a lady by public references. A niece who remembered "her loving, gentle disposition" emphasized "her modest, even timid manner." Church records preserve some details of her life; she seems to have considered formal church affiliation a matter of importance.

Angelica Singleton Van Buren: daughter-in-law and hostess of the widower President.

She bore a son in Kinderhook, three others in Hudson, where Martin served as county surrogate; but the fourth son died in infancy. In 1816 the family moved to the state capital in Albany. Soon the household included Martin's law partner and three apprentices; relatives came and went constantly, and Hannah could return their visits. Contemporary letters indicate that she was busy, sociable, and happy. She gave birth to a fifth boy in January 1817.

But by the following winter her health was obviously failing, apparently from tuberculosis. Not yet 36, she died on February 5, 1819. The Albany *Argus* called her "an ornament of the Christian faith."

Her husband never remarried; he moved into the White House in 1837 as a widower with four bachelor sons. Now accustomed to living in elegant style, he immediately began to refurbish a mansion shabby from public use under Jackson. Across Lafayette Square, Dolley Madison reigned as matriarch of Washington society; when her young relative-by-marriage Angelica Singleton came up from South Carolina for a visit, Dolley took her to the White House to pay a call.

Angelica's aristocratic manners, excellent education, and handsome face won the heart of the President's eldest son, Abraham. They were married in November 1838; next spring a honeymoon abroad polished her social experience. Thereafter, while Abraham served as the President's private secretary, Angelica presided as lady of the house. The only flaw in her pleasure in this role was the loss of a baby girl. Born at the White House, she lived only a few hours. In later years, though spending much time in South Carolina and in Europe, Angelica and her husband made their home in New York City; she died there in 1878.

"Jannetje," Martin Van Buren called his wife, in the Dutch language of their ancestors. An unknown artist painted two portraits of her: one for her husband, one for her niece Maria Hoes Cantine. Initials on the back of the gold brooch indicate that this belonged to the niece; an inset holds a plaited lock of reddish-brown hair, probably a memento of "Aunt Hannah." Prolonged illness, almost certainly tuberculosis, claimed Hannah Van Buren at age 35: years later, Maria remembered "the perfect composure" of her deathbed farewell to her children, and her wish that money usually spent on gifts to pallbearers "should be given to the poor."

Anna Tuthill Symmes Harrison
1775-1864

Anna Harrison was too ill to travel when her husband set out from Ohio in 1841 for his inauguration. It was a long trip and a difficult one even by steamboat and railroad, with February weather uncertain at best, and she at age 65 was well acquainted with the rigors of frontier journeys.

As a girl of 19, bringing pretty clothes and dainty manners, she went out to Ohio with her father, Judge John Cleves Symmes, who had taken up land for settlement on the "north bend" of the Ohio River. She had grown up a young lady of the East, completing her education at a boarding school in New York City.

A clandestine marriage on November 25, 1795, united Anna Symmes and Lt. William Henry Harrison, an experienced soldier at 22. Though the young man came from one of the best families of Virginia, Judge Symmes did not want his daughter to face the hard life of frontier forts; but eventually, seeing her happiness, he accepted her choice.

Hostess for a single month: Jane Irwin Harrison, portrayed by an unknown artist.

Though Harrison won fame as an Indian fighter and hero of the War of 1812, he spent much of his life in a civilian career. His service in Congress as territorial delegate from Ohio gave Anna and their two children a chance to visit his family at Berkeley, their plantation on the James River. Her third child was born on that trip, at Richmond in September 1800. Harrison's appointment as governor of Indiana Territory took them even farther into the wilderness; he built a handsome house at Vincennes that blended fortress and plantation mansion. Five more children were born to Anna.

Facing war in 1812, the family went to the farm at North Bend. Before peace was assured, she had borne two more children. There, at news of her husband's landslide electoral victory in 1840, home-loving Anna said simply: "I wish that my husband's friends had left him where he is, happy and contented in retirement."

When she decided not to go to Washington with him, the President-elect asked his daughter-in-law Jane Irwin Harrison, widow of his namesake son, to accompany him and act as hostess until Anna's proposed arrival in May. Half a dozen other relatives happily went with them. On April 4, exactly one month after his inauguration, he died, so Anna never made the journey. She had already begun her packing when she learned of her loss.

Accepting grief with admirable dignity, she stayed at her home in North Bend until the house burned in 1858; she lived nearby with her last surviving child, John Scott Harrison, until she died in February 1864 at the age of 88.

Dressed in mourning, Anna Harrison posed for Cornelia Stuart Cassady in 1843—possibly at the Ohio home she had not left during her husband's Presidency. Her health precarious in 1841, she had temporarily entrusted the duties of White House hostess to her widowed daughter-in-law, Jane Irwin Harrison; before she could assume them herself, her husband died.

Heirloom portrait survived Civil War hazards to record the tranquil charm of Letitia Tyler for her descendants. An unknown artist painted it sometime before a paralytic stroke crippled her in 1839. At the White House she lived in seclusion. Her first daughter-in-law, Priscilla Cooper Tyler, assumed the duties of hostess until 1844, when she moved to Philadelphia. Between Letitia Tyler's death in 1842 and her husband's second marriage, the role of First Lady passed briefly to her second daughter, Letitia Tyler Semple.

Letitia Christian Tyler
1790-1842

Letitia Tyler had been confined to an invalid's chair for two years when her husband unexpectedly became President. Nobody had thought of that possibility when he took his oath of office as Vice President on March 4, 1841; indeed, he had planned to fill his undemanding duties from his home in Williamsburg where his wife was most comfortable, her Bible, prayer book, and knitting at her side.

Born on a Tidewater Virginia plantation in the 18th century, Letitia was spiritually akin to Martha Washington and Martha Jefferson. Formal education was no part of this pattern of life, but Letitia learned all the skills of managing a plantation, rearing a family, and presiding over a home that would be John Tyler's refuge during an active political life. They were married on March 29, 1813 — his twenty-third birthday. Thereafter, whether he served in Congress or as Governor of Virginia, she attended to domestic duties. Only once did she join him for the winter social season in Washington. Of the eight children she bore, seven survived; but after 1839 she was a cripple, though "still beautiful now in her declining years."

So her admiring new daughter-in-law, Priscilla Cooper Tyler, described her — "the most entirely unselfish person you can imagine.... Notwithstanding her very delicate health, mother attends to and regulates all the household affairs and all so quietly that you can't tell when she does it."

In a second-floor room at the White House, Letitia Tyler kept her quiet but pivotal role in family activities. She did not attempt to take part in the social affairs of the administration. Her married daughters had their own homes; the others were too young for the full responsibility of official entertaining; Priscilla at age 24 assumed the position of White House hostess, met its demands with spirit and success, and enjoyed it.

Daughter of a well-known tragedian, Priscilla Cooper had gone on the stage herself at 17. Playing Desdemona to her father's Othello in Richmond, she won the instant interest of Robert Tyler, whom she married in 1839. Intelligent and beautiful, with dark brown hair, she charmed the President's guests — from visiting celebrities like Charles Dickens to enthusiastic countrymen. Once she noted ruefully: "such hearty shakes as they gave my poor little hand too!" She enjoyed the expert advice of Dolley Madison, and the companionship of her young sister-in-law Elizabeth until she married William N. Waller in 1842.

For this wedding Letitia made her only appearance at a White House social function. "Lizzie looked surpassingly lovely," said Priscilla, and "our dear mother" was "far more attractive to me ... than any other lady in the room," greeting her guests "in her sweet, gentle, self-possessed manner."

The first President's wife to die in the White House, Letitia Tyler ended her days peacefully on September 10, 1842, holding a damask rose in her hand. She was taken to Virginia for burial at the plantation of her birth, deeply mourned by her family. "She had everything about her," said Priscilla, "to awaken love...."

Julia Gardiner Tyler
1820-1889

"I grieve my love a belle should be," sighed one of Julia Gardiner's innumerable admirers in 1840; at the age of 20 she was already famous as the "Rose of Long Island."

Daughter of Juliana McLachlan and David Gardiner, descendant of prominent and wealthy New York families, Julia was trained from earliest childhood for a life in society; she made her debut at 15. A European tour with her family gave her new glimpses of social splendors. Late in 1842 the Gardiners went to Washington for the winter social season, and Julia became the undisputed darling of the capital. Her beauty and her practiced charm attracted the most eminent men in the city, among them President Tyler, a widower since September.

Tragedy brought his courtship poignant success the next winter. Julia, her sister Margaret, and her father joined a Presidential excursion on the new steam frigate *Princeton;* and David Gardiner lost his life in the explosion of a huge naval gun. Tyler comforted Julia in her grief and won her consent to a secret engagement.

The first President to marry in office took his vows in New York on June 26, 1844. The news was then broken to the American people, who greeted it with keen interest, much publicity, and some criticism about the couple's difference in age: 30 years.

As young Mrs. Tyler said herself, she "reigned" as First Lady for the last eight months of her husband's term. Wearing white satin or black lace to obey the conventions of mourning, she presided with vivacity and animation at a series of parties. She enjoyed her position immensely, and filled it with grace. For receptions she revived the formality of the Van Buren administration; she welcomed her guests with plumes in her hair, attended by maids of honor dressed in white. She once declared, with truth: "Nothing appears to delight the President more than . . . to hear people sing my praises."

The Tylers' happiness was unshaken when they retired to their home at Sherwood Forest in Virginia. There Julia bore five of her seven children; and she acted as mistress of the plantation until the Civil War. As such, she defended both states' rights and the institution of slavery. She championed the political views of her husband, who remained for her "the President" until the end of his life.

His death in 1862 came as a severe blow to her. In a poem composed for his sixty-second birthday she had assured him that "what e'er changes time may bring, I'll love thee as thou art!"

Even as a refugee in New York, she devoted herself to volunteer work for the Confederacy. Its defeat found her impoverished. Not until 1958 would federal law provide automatic pensions for Presidential widows; but Congress in 1870 voted a pension for Mary Lincoln, and Julia Tyler used this precedent in seeking help. In December 1880 Congress voted her $1,200 a year—and after Garfield's assassination it passed bills to grant uniform amounts of $5,000 annually to Mrs. Garfield, Mrs. Lincoln, Mrs. Polk, and Mrs. Tyler. Living out her last years comfortably in Richmond, Julia died there in 1889 and was buried there at her husband's side.

"Most beautiful woman of the age and . . . most accomplished," President
*Tyler called his new bride, who keenly enjoyed her success as hostess at
the White House. She posed for this portrait three years after leaving it.*

"Time has dealt kindly with her personal charms. . . ," declared one of many admiring citizens when Sarah Polk became First Lady. In 1846 both she and her husband posed at the White House for George P. A. Healy; three years later they took his fine portraits home to "Polk Place" in Nashville, Tennessee. In her 80th year, ladies of the state commissioned a copy of hers for the Executive Mansion; they entrusted the work to George Dury, who had already painted her at 75—still handsome and alert. Revered throughout the land, she kept her dignity of manner and her clarity of mind to the end.

Sarah Childress Polk
1803-1891

Silks and satins little Sarah took for granted, growing up on a plantation near Murfreesboro, Tennessee. Elder daughter of Captain Joel and Elizabeth Childress, she gained something rarer from her father's wealth. He sent her and her sister away to school, first to Nashville, then to the Moravians' "female academy" at Salem, North Carolina, one of the very few institutions of higher learning available to women in the early 19th century. So she acquired an education that made her especially fitted to assist a man with a political career.

James K. Polk was laying the foundation for that career when he met her. He had begun his first year's service in the Tennessee legislature when they were married on New Year's Day, 1824; he was 28, she 20. The story goes that Andrew Jackson had encouraged their romance; he certainly made Polk a political protégé, and as such Polk represented a district in Congress for 14 sessions.

In an age when motherhood gave a woman her only acknowledged career, Sarah Polk had to resign herself to childlessness. Moreover, no lady would admit to a political role of her own, but Mrs. Polk found scope for her astute mind as well as her social skills. She accompanied her husband to Washington whenever she could, and they soon won a place in its most select social circles. Constantly—but privately—Sarah was helping him with his speeches, copying his correspondence, giving him advice. Much as she enjoyed politics, she would warn him against overwork. He would hand her a newspaper—"Sarah, here is something I wish you to read. . . ."—and she would set to work as well.

A devout Presbyterian, she refused to attend horse races or the theater; but she always maintained social contacts of value to James. When he returned to Washington as President in 1845, she stepped to her high position with ease and evident pleasure. She appeared at the inaugural ball, but did not dance.

Contrasted with Julia Tyler's waltzes, her entertainments have become famous for sedateness and sobriety. Some later accounts say that the Polks never served wine, but in December 1845 a Congressman's wife recorded in her diary details of a four-hour dinner for forty at the White House—glasses for six different wines, from pink champagne to ruby port and sauterne, "formed a rainbow around each plate." Skilled in tactful conversation, Mrs. Polk enjoyed wide popularity as well as deep respect.

Only three months after retirement to their fine new home "Polk Place" in Nashville, he died, worn out by years of public service. Clad always in black, Sarah Polk lived on in that home for 42 years, guarding the memory of her husband and accepting honors paid to her as honors due to him. The house became a place of pilgrimage.

During the Civil War, Mrs. Polk held herself above sectional strife and received with dignity leaders of both Confederate and Union armies; all respected Polk Place as neutral ground. She presided over her house until her death in her 88th year. Buried beside her husband, she was mourned by a nation that had come to regard her as a precious link to the past.

Margaret Mackall Smith Taylor
1788-1852

After the election of 1848, a passenger on a Mississippi riverboat struck up a conversation with easy-mannered Gen. Zachary Taylor, not knowing his identity. The passenger remarked that he didn't think the general qualified for the Presidency—was the stranger "a Taylor man"? "Not much of a one," came the reply. The general went on to say that he hadn't voted for Taylor, partly because his wife was opposed to sending "Old Zack" to Washington, "where she would be obliged to go with him!" It was a truthful answer.

Moreover, the story goes that Margaret Taylor had taken a vow during the Mexican War: If her husband returned safely, she would never go into society again. In fact she never did, though prepared for it by genteel upbringing.

"Peggy" Smith was born in Calvert County, Maryland, daughter of Ann Mackall and Walter Smith, a major in the Revolutionary War according to family tradition. In 1809, visiting a sister in Kentucky, she met young Lieutenant Taylor. They were married the following June, and for a while the young wife stayed on the farm given them as a wedding present by Zachary's father. She bore her first baby there, but cheerfully followed her husband from one remote garrison to another along the western frontier of civilization. An admiring civilian official cited her as one of the "delicate females . . . reared in tenderness" who had to educate "worthy and most interesting" children at a fort in Indian country.

Two small girls died in 1820 of what Taylor called "a violent bilious fever," which left their mother's health impaired; three girls and a boy grew up. Knowing the hardships of a military wife, Taylor opposed his daughters' marrying career soldiers— but each eventually married into the Army.

The second daughter, Knox, married Lt. Jefferson Davis in gentle defiance of her parents. In a loving letter home, she imagined her mother skimming milk in the cellar or going out to feed the chickens. Within three months of her wedding, Knox died of malaria. Taylor was not reconciled to Davis until they fought together in Mexico; in Washington the second Mrs. Davis became a good friend of Mrs. Taylor's, often calling on her at the White House.

Though Peggy Taylor welcomed friends and kinfolk in her upstairs sitting room, presided at the family table, met special groups at her husband's side, and worshiped regularly at St. John's Episcopal Church, she took no part in formal social functions. She relegated all the duties of official hostess to her youngest daughter, Mary Elizabeth, then 25 and recent bride of Lt. Col. William W. S. Bliss, adjutant and secretary to the President. Betty Bliss filled her role admirably. One observer thought that her manner blended "the artlessness of a rustic belle and the grace of a duchess."

For Mrs. Taylor, her husband's death—on July 9, 1850—was an appalling blow. Never again did she speak of the White House. She spent her last days with the Blisses, dying on August 18, 1852.

Hostess in her mother's stead, Betty Taylor Bliss probably posed for this daguerreotype about a decade after her White House days. Of Mrs. Taylor, a semi-invalid for years, no authentic likeness survives; contemporaries described her as slender and stately, a brunette in youth.

Dignity of a matron in middle life marks this likeness of Abigail Fillmore, rendered in oils by an unknown artist—possibly copying a photograph. By contemporary descriptions she had been fair of coloring and taller at 5 feet 6 inches than the average woman of her time. A snippet of Washington gossip suggests her manner as First Lady, accusing her of lacking "good form" in seeming "so motherly to her guests." In the duties of hostess her daughter Mary Abigail gave her welcome help. "Abby," a talented young woman of poise and polish, managed the former President's household from her mother's death until her own shockingly unexpected death at age 22. After five years Fillmore found escape from loneliness in a second happy marriage: to Caroline Carmichael McIntosh, a wealthy and childless widow who survived him.

Abigail Powers Fillmore
1798-1853

First of First Ladies to hold a job after marriage, Abigail Fillmore was helping her husband's career. She was also revealing her most striking personal characteristic: eagerness to learn and pleasure in teaching others.

She was born in Saratoga County, New York, in 1798, while it was still on the fringe of civilization. Her father, a locally prominent Baptist preacher named Lemuel Powers, died shortly thereafter. Courageously, her mother moved on westward, thinking her scanty funds would go further in a less settled region, and ably educated her small son and daughter beyond the usual frontier level with the help of her husband's library.

Shared eagerness for schooling formed a bond when Abigail Powers at 21 met Millard Fillmore at 19, both students at a recently opened academy in the village of New Hope. Although she soon became young Fillmore's inspiration, his struggle to make his way as a lawyer was so long and ill-paid that they were not married until February 1826. She even resumed teaching school after the marriage. And then her only son, Millard Powers, was born in 1828.

Attaining prosperity at last, Fillmore bought his family a six-room house in Buffalo, where little Mary Abigail was born in 1832. Enjoying comparative luxury, Abigail learned the ways of society as the wife of a Congressman. She cultivated a noted flower garden; but much of her time, as always, she spent in reading. In 1847, Fillmore was elected state comptroller; with the children away in boarding school and college, the parents moved temporarily to Albany.

In 1849, Abigail Fillmore came to Washington as wife of the Vice President; 16 months later, after Zachary Taylor's death at a height of sectional crisis, the Fillmores moved into the White House.

Even after the period of official mourning the social life of the Fillmore administration remained subdued. The First Lady presided with grace at state dinners and receptions; but a permanently injured ankle made her Friday-evening levees an ordeal—two hours of standing at her husband's side to greet the public. In any case, she preferred reading or music in private. Pleading her delicate health, she entrusted many routine social duties to her attractive daughter, "Abby." With a special appropriation from Congress, she spent contented hours selecting books for a White House library and arranging them in the oval room upstairs, where Abby had her piano, harp, and guitar. Here, wrote a friend, Mrs. Fillmore "could enjoy the music she so much loved, and the conversation of . . . cultivated society. . . ."

Despite chronic poor health, Mrs. Fillmore stayed near her husband through the outdoor ceremonies of President Pierce's inauguration while a raw northeast wind whipped snow over the crowd. Returning chilled to the Willard Hotel, she developed pneumonia; she died there on March 30, 1853. The House of Representatives and the Senate adjourned, and public offices closed in respect, as her family took her body home to Buffalo for burial.

Jane Means Appleton Pierce
1806-1863

In looks and in pathetic destiny young Jane Means Appleton resembled the heroine of a Victorian novel. The gentle dignity of her face reflected her sensitive, retiring personality and physical weakness. Her father had died—he was a Congregational minister, the Reverend Jesse Appleton, president of Bowdoin College—and her mother had taken the family to Amherst, New Hampshire. And Jane met a Bowdoin graduate, a young lawyer with political ambitions, Franklin Pierce.

Although he was immediately devoted to Jane, they did not marry until she was 28—surprising in that day of early marriages. Her family opposed the match; moreover, she always did her best to discourage his interest in politics. The death of a three-day-old son, the arrival of a new baby, and Jane's dislike of Washington counted heavily in his decision to retire at the apparent height of his career, as United States Senator, in 1842. Little Frank Robert, the second son, died the next year of typhus.

Service in the Mexican War brought Pierce the rank of brigadier and local fame as a hero. He returned home safely, and for four years the Pierces lived quietly at Concord, New Hampshire, in the happiest period of their lives. With attentive pleasure Jane watched her son Benjamin growing up.

Then, in 1852, the Democratic Party made Pierce their candidate for President. His wife fainted at the news. When he took her to Newport for a respite, Benny wrote to her: "I hope he won't be elected for I should not like to be at Washington and I know you would not either." But the President-elect convinced Jane that his office would be an asset for Benny's success in life.

On a journey by train, January 6, 1853, their car was derailed and Benny killed before their eyes. The whole nation shared the parents' grief. The inauguration on March 4 took place without an inaugural ball and without the presence of Mrs. Pierce. She joined her husband later that month, but any pleasure the White House might have brought her was gone. From this loss she never recovered fully. Other events deepened the somber mood of the new administration: Mrs. Fillmore's death in March, that of Vice President Rufus King in April.

Always devout, Jane Pierce turned for solace to prayer. She had to force herself to meet the social obligations inherent in the role of First Lady. Fortunately she had the companionship and help of a girlhood friend, now her aunt by marriage, Abigail Kent Means. Mrs. Robert E. Lee wrote in a private letter: "I have known many of the ladies of the White House, none more truly excellent than the afflicted wife of President Pierce. Her health was a bar to any great effort on her part to meet the expectations of the public in her high position but she was a refined, extremely religious and well educated lady."

With retirement, the Pierces made a prolonged trip abroad in search of health for the invalid—she carried Benny's Bible throughout the journey. The quest was unsuccessful, so the couple came home to New Hampshire to be near family and friends until Jane's death in 1863. She was buried near Benny's grave.

Treasure for a family's annals, this likeness—a photograph from about 1850 —captures the mutual devotion of Jane Pierce and Benny, last of her three sons. Two months before Pierce's inauguration, a railroad accident killed 11-year-old Benny before his parents' eyes. When his stricken mother finally brought herself to appear at White House functions, the guests who acknowledged her "winning smile" could not fail to recognize the "traces of bereavement . . . on a countenance too ingenuous for concealment. . . ."

Harriet Lane
1830-1903

Unique among First Ladies, Harriet Lane acted as hostess for the only President who never married: James Buchanan, her favorite uncle and her guardian after she was orphaned at the age of eleven. And of all the ladies of the White House, few achieved such great success in deeply troubled times as this polished young woman in her twenties.

In the rich farming country of Franklin County, Pennsylvania, her family had prospered as merchants. Her uncle supervised her sound education in private school, completed by two years at the Visitation Convent in Georgetown. By this time "Nunc" was Secretary of State, and he introduced her to fashionable circles as he had promised, "in the best manner." In 1854 she joined him in London, where he was minister to the Court of St. James's. Queen Victoria gave "dear Miss Lane" the rank of ambassador's wife; admiring suitors gave her the fame of a beauty.

In appearance "Hal" Lane was of medium height, with masses of light hair almost golden. In manner she enlivened social gatherings with a captivating mixture of spontaneity and poise.

After the sadness of the Pierce administration, the capital eagerly welcomed its new "Democratic Queen" in 1857. Harriet Lane filled the White House with gaiety and flowers, and guided its social life with enthusiasm and discretion, winning national popularity.

As sectional tensions increased, she worked out seating arrangements for her weekly formal dinner parties with special care, to give dignitaries their proper precedence and still keep political foes apart. Her tact did not falter, but her task became impossible—as did her uncle's. Seven states had seceded by the time Buchanan retired from office and thankfully returned with his niece to his spacious country home, "Wheatland."

From her teen-age years, the popular Miss Lane flirted happily with numerous beaux, calling them "pleasant but dreadfully troublesome." Buchanan often warned her against "rushing precipitately into matrimonial connexions," and she waited until she was almost 36 to marry. She chose, with her uncle's approval, Henry Elliott Johnston, a Baltimore banker. Within the next 18 years she faced one sorrow after another: the loss of her uncle, her two fine young sons, and her husband.

Thereafter she decided to live in Washington, among friends made during years of happiness. She had acquired a sizable art collection, largely of European works, which she bequeathed to the government. Accepted after her death in 1903, it inspired an official of the Smithsonian Institution to call her "First Lady of the National Collection of Fine Arts." In addition, she had dedicated a generous sum to endow a "home for invalid children" at the Johns Hopkins Hospital in Baltimore; it became an outstanding pediatrics facility, and its national reputation was a fitting memorial to the girl who presided at the White House with such dignity and charm. The Harriet Lane Home Clinic serves thousands of children today.

"Mischievous romp of a niece," James Buchanan once called the little tomboy who at age 26 became White House hostess for the bachelor President. Artist John Henry Brown captured her queenly beauty 21 years after Harriet Lane assumed the role of First Lady. Fun-loving and flirtatious, spending lavishly on parties and clothes, she brightened a gloomy administration as civil war threatened it, warning her guests to refrain from political discussions.

Mary Todd Lincoln
1818-1882

As a girlhood companion remembered her, Mary Todd was vivacious and impulsive, with an interesting personality—but "she now and then could not restrain a witty, sarcastic speech that cut deeper than she intended...." A young lawyer summed her up in 1840: "the very creature of excitement." All of these attributes marked her life, bringing her both happiness and tragedy.

Daughter of Eliza Parker and Robert Smith Todd, pioneer settlers of Kentucky, Mary lost her mother before the age of seven. Her father remarried; and Mary remembered her childhood as "desolate" although she belonged to the aristocracy of Lexington, with high-spirited social life and a sound private education.

Just 5 feet 2 inches at maturity, Mary had clear blue eyes, long lashes, light-brown hair with glints of bronze, and a lovely complexion. She danced gracefully, she loved finery, and her crisp intelligence polished the wiles of a Southern coquette.

Nearly 21, she went to Springfield, Illinois, to live with her sister Mrs. Ninian Edwards. Here she met Abraham Lincoln—in his own words, "a poor nobody then." Three years later, after a stormy courtship and broken engagement, they were married. Though opposites in background and temperament, they were united by an enduring love—by Mary's confidence in her husband's ability and his gentle consideration of her excitable ways.

Their years in Springfield brought hard work, a family of boys, and reduced circumstances to the pleasure-loving girl who had never felt responsibility before. Lincoln's single term in Congress, for 1847-1849, gave Mary and the boys a winter in Washington, but scant opportunity for social life. Finally her unwavering faith in her husband won ample justification with his election as President in 1860.

Though her position fulfilled her high social ambitions, Mrs. Lincoln's years in the White House mingled misery with triumph. An orgy of spending stirred resentful comment. While the Civil War dragged on, Southerners scorned her as a traitor to her birth, and citizens loyal to the Union suspected her of treason. When she entertained, critics accused her of unpatriotic extravagance. When, utterly distraught, she curtailed her entertaining after her son Willie's death in 1862, they accused her of shirking her social duties.

Yet Lincoln, watching her put her guests at ease during a White House reception, could say happily: "My wife is as handsome as when she was a girl, and I . . . fell in love with her; and what is more, I have never fallen out."

Her husband's assassination in 1865 shattered Mary Todd Lincoln. The next 17 years held nothing but sorrow. With her son "Tad" she traveled abroad in search of health, tortured by distorted ideas of her financial situation. After Tad died in 1871, she slipped into a world of illusion where poverty and murder pursued her.

A misunderstood and tragic figure, she passed away in 1882 at her sister's home in Springfield—the same house from which she had walked as the bride of Abraham Lincoln, 40 years before.

Mathew Brady's camera reveals Mary Lincoln before hostile gossip, private grief, and national tragedy had marked her face—probably in 1861. Of six portraits he made that year, she found only a profile "passable."

Married at 16, Eliza McCardle Johnson taught her husband writing and arithmetic. In poor health when she went to the White House, she left the duties of First Lady to her daughter Martha Patterson (opposite), who modestly said of her family: "We are plain people, from the mountains of Tennessee, called here for a short time by a national calamity. I trust too much will not be expected of us." Byrd Venable Farioletti painted Mrs. Johnson's portrait in 1961, from a photograph taken during the White House years.

Eliza McCardle Johnson
1810-1876

"I knew he'd be acquitted; I knew it," declared Eliza McCardle Johnson, told how the Senate had voted in her husband's impeachment trial. Her faith in him had never wavered during those difficult days in 1868, when her courage dictated that all White House social events should continue as usual.

That faith began to develop many years before in east Tennessee, when Andrew Johnson first came to Greeneville, across the mountains from North Carolina, and established a tailor shop. Eliza was almost 16 then and Andrew only 17; and local tradition tells of the day she first saw him. He was driving a blind pony hitched to a small cart, and she said to a girl friend, "There goes my beau!" She married him within a year, on May 17, 1827.

Eliza was the daughter of Sarah Phillips and John McCardle, a shoemaker. Fortunately she had received a good basic education that she was delighted to share with her new husband. He already knew his letters and could read a bit, so she taught him writing and arithmetic. With their limited means, her skill at keeping a house and bringing up a family—five children, in all—had much to do with Johnson's success.

He rose rapidly, serving in the state and national legislatures and as governor. Like him, when the Civil War came, people of east Tennessee remained loyal to the Union; Lincoln sent him to Nashville as military governor in 1862. Rebel forces caught Eliza at home with part of the family. Only after months of uncertainty did they rejoin Andrew Johnson in Nashville. By 1865 a soldier son and son-in-law had died, and Eliza was an invalid for life.

Quite aside from the tragedy of Lincoln's death, she found little pleasure in her husband's position as President. At the White House, she settled into a second-floor room that became the center of activities for a large

Martha Johnson Patterson, wearing onyx earrings that Mrs. Polk had given to her.

family: her two sons, her widowed daughter Mary Stover and her children; her older daughter Martha with her husband, Senator David T. Patterson, and their children. As a schoolgirl Martha had often been the Polks' guest at the mansion; now she took up its social duties. She was a competent, unpretentious, and gracious hostess even during the impeachment crisis.

At the end of Johnson's term, Eliza returned with relief to her home in Tennessee, restored from wartime vandalism. She lived to see the legislature of her state vindicate her husband's career by electing him to the Senate in 1875, and survived him by nearly six months, dying at the Pattersons' home in 1876.

43

Julia Dent Grant
1826-1902

Quite naturally, shy young Lieutenant Grant lost his heart to friendly Julia; and he made his love known, as he said himself years later, "in the most awkward manner imaginable." She told her side of the story—her father opposed the match, saying, "the boy is too poor," and she answered angrily that she was poor herself. The "poverty" on her part came from a slaveowner's lack of ready cash.

Daughter of Frederick and Ellen Wrenshall Dent, Julia had grown up on a plantation near St. Louis in a typically Southern atmosphere. In memoirs prepared late in life—unpublished until 1975—she pictured her girlhood as an idyll: "one long summer of sunshine, flowers, and smiles. . . ." She attended the Misses Mauros' boarding school in St. Louis for seven years among the daughters of other affluent parents. A social favorite in that circle, she met "Ulys" at her home, where her family welcomed him as a West Point classmate of her brother Frederick; soon she felt lonely without him, dreamed of him, and agreed to wear his West Point ring.

Julia and her handsome lieutenant became engaged in 1844, but the Mexican War deferred the wedding for four long years. Their marriage, often tried by adversity, met every test; they gave each other a life-long loyalty. Like other army wives, "dearest Julia" accompanied her husband to military posts, to pass uneventful days at distant garrisons. Then she returned to his parents' home in 1852 when he was ordered to the West.

Ending that separation, Grant resigned his commission two years later. Farming and business ventures at St. Louis failed, and in 1860 he took his family—four children now—back to his home in Galena, Illinois. He was working in his father's leather goods store when the Civil War called him to a soldier's duty with his state's volunteers. Throughout the war, Julia joined her husband near the scene of action whenever she could.

After so many years of hardship and stress, she rejoiced in his fame as a victorious general, and she entered the White House in 1869 to begin, in her words, "the happiest period" of her life. With Cabinet wives as her allies, she entertained extensively and lavishly. Contemporaries noted her finery, jewels and silks and laces.

Upon leaving the White House in 1877, the Grants made a trip around the world that became a journey of triumphs. Julia proudly recalled details of hospitality and magnificent gifts they received.

But in 1884 Grant suffered yet another business failure and they lost all they had. To provide for his wife, Grant wrote his famous personal memoirs, racing with time and death from cancer. The means thus afforded and her widow's pension enabled her to live in comfort, surrounded by children and grandchildren, till her own death in 1902. She had attended in 1897 the dedication of Grant's monumental tomb in New York City where she was laid to rest. She had ended her own chronicle of their years together with a firm declaration: "the light of his glorious fame still reaches out to me, falls upon me, and warms me."

At Mathew Brady's studio, Julia Dent Grant adopts a characteristic pose to hide an eye defect. Grant rejected the idea of corrective surgery, teasing her gently: "...I might not like you half so well with any other eyes."

Lucy Ware Webb Hayes
1831-1889

There was no inaugural ball in 1877—when Rutherford B. Hayes and his wife, Lucy, left Ohio for Washington, the outcome of the election was still in doubt. Public fears had not subsided when it was settled in Hayes' favor; and when Lucy watched her husband take his oath of office at the Capitol, her serene and beautiful face impressed even cynical journalists.

She came to the White House well-loved by many. Born in Chillicothe, Ohio, daughter of Maria Cook and Dr. James Webb, she lost her father at age two. She was just entering her teens when Mrs. Webb took her sons to the town of Delaware to enroll in the new Ohio Wesleyan University, but she began studying with its excellent instructors. She graduated from the Wesleyan Female College in Cincinnati at 18, unusually well-educated for a young lady of her day.

"Rud" Hayes at 27 had set up a law practice in Cincinnati, and he began paying calls at the Webb home. References to Lucy appeared in his diary: "Her low sweet voice is very winning...a heart as true as steel.... Intellect she has too.... By George! I am in love with her!" Married in 1852, they lived in Cincinnati until the Civil War, and he soon came to share her deeply religious opposition to slavery. Visits to relatives and vacation journeys broke the routine of a happy domestic life in a growing family. Over twenty years Lucy bore eight children, of whom five grew up.

She won the affectionate name of "Mother Lucy" from men of the 23rd Ohio Volunteer Infantry who served under her husband's command in the war. They remembered her visits to camp—to minister to the wounded, cheer the homesick, and comfort the dying. Hayes' distinguished combat record earned him election to Congress, and three postwar terms as governor of Ohio. She not only joined him in Washington for its winter social season, she also accompanied him on visits to state reform schools, prisons, and asylums. As the popular first lady of her state, she gained experience in what a woman of her time aptly called "semi-public life."

Thus she entered the White House with confidence gained from her long and happy married life, her knowledge of political circles, her intelligence and culture, and her cheerful spirit. She enjoyed informal parties, and spared no effort to make official entertaining attractive. Though she was a temperance advocate and liquor was banned at the mansion during this administration, she was a very popular hostess. She took criticism of her views in good humor (the famous nickname "Lemonade Lucy" apparently came into use only after she had left the mansion). She became one of the best-loved women to preside over the White House, where the Hayeses celebrated their silver wedding anniversary in 1877, and an admirer hailed her as representing "the new woman era."

The Hayes term ended in 1881, and the family home was now "Spiegel Grove," an estate at Fremont, Ohio. There husband and wife spent eight active, contented years together until her death in 1889. She was buried in Fremont, mourned by her family and hosts of friends.

Sunny in temperament, winning in manner, firm in high principle, Lucy Hayes met both praise and gibes when White House menus omitted liquor. The Woman's Christian Temperance Union honored her with this portrait.

Intellectual Lucretia Garfield—"Crete" to the husband who depended upon her political insights—may have posed for this Brady study while still a Congressman's wife. Illness and turmoil filled her 200 days as First Lady.

Lucretia Rudolph Garfield
1832-1918

In the fond eyes of her husband, President James A. Garfield, Lucretia "grows up to every new emergency with fine tact and faultless taste." She proved this in the eyes of the nation, though she was always a reserved, self-contained woman. She flatly refused to pose for a campaign photograph, and much preferred a literary circle or informal party to a state reception.

Her love of learning she acquired from her father, Zeb Rudolph, a leading citizen of Hiram, Ohio, and devout member of the Disciples of Christ. She first met "Jim" Garfield when both attended a nearby school, and they renewed their friendship in 1851 as students at the Western Reserve Eclectic Institute, founded by the Disciples.

But "Crete" did not attract his special attention until December 1853, when he began a rather cautious courtship, and they did not marry until November 1858, when he was well-launched on his career as a teacher. His service in the Union Army from 1861 to 1863 kept them apart; their first child, a daughter, died in 1863. But after his first lonely winter in Washington as a freshman Representative, the family remained together. With a home in the capital as well as one in Ohio they enjoyed a happy domestic life. A two-year-old son died in 1876, but five children grew up healthy and promising; with the passage of time, Lucretia became more and more her husband's companion.

In Washington they shared intellectual interests with congenial friends; she went with him to meetings of a locally celebrated literary society. They read together, made social calls together, dined with each other and traveled in company until by 1880 they were as nearly inseparable as his career permitted.

Garfield's election to the Presidency brought a cheerful family to the White House in 1881. Though Mrs. Garfield was not particularly interested in a First Lady's social duties, she was deeply conscientious and her genuine hospitality made her dinners and twice-weekly receptions enjoyable. At the age of 49 she was still a slender, graceful little woman with clear dark eyes, her brown hair beginning to show traces of silver.

In May she fell gravely ill, apparently from malaria and nervous exhaustion, to her husband's profound distress. "When you are sick," he had written her seven years earlier, "I am like the inhabitants of countries visited by earthquakes." She was still a convalescent, at a seaside resort in New Jersey, when he was shot by a demented assassin on July 2. She returned to Washington by special train—"frail, fatigued, desperate," reported an eyewitness at the White House, "but firm and quiet and full of purpose to save."

During the three months her husband fought for his life, her grief, devotion, and fortitude won the respect and sympathy of the country. In September, after his death, the bereaved family went home to their farm in Ohio. For another 36 years she led a strictly private but busy and comfortable life, active in preserving the records of her husband's career. She died on March 14, 1918.

Daily throughout his White House years, according to family tradition, President Chester A. Arthur had a fresh bouquet of flowers placed before this hand-tinted, silver-framed photograph of his wife. Ellen Herndon Arthur had died ten months before his election to the Vice Presidency. A sophisticated host in his own right, he asked his sister Mary McElroy to assume the role of White House hostess for form's sake, and to oversee the care of his motherless daughter, Ellen.

Ellen Lewis Herndon Arthur
1837-1880

Chester Alan Arthur's beloved "Nell" died of pneumonia on January 12, 1880. That November, when he was elected Vice President, he was still mourning her bitterly. In his own words: "Honors to me now are not what they once were." His grief was the more poignant because she was only 42 and her death sudden. Just two days earlier she had attended a benefit concert in New York City—while he was busy with politics in Albany—and she caught cold that night while waiting for her carriage. She was already unconscious when he reached her side.

Her family connections among distinguished Virginians had shaped her life. She was born at Culpeper Court House, only child of Elizabeth Hansbrough and William Lewis Herndon, U.S.N. They moved to Washington, D. C., when he was assigned to help his brother-in-law Lt. Matthew Fontaine Maury establish the Naval Observatory. While Ellen was still just a girl her beautiful contralto voice attracted attention; she joined the choir at St. John's Episcopal Church on Lafayette Square.

Then her father assumed command of a mail steamer operating from New York; and in 1856 a cousin introduced her to "Chet" Arthur, who was establishing a law practice in the city. By 1857 they were engaged. In a birthday letter that year he reminded her of "the soft, moonlight nights of June, a year ago . . . happy, happy days at Saratoga —the golden, fleeting hours at Lake George." He wished he could hear her singing.

That same year her father died a hero's death at sea, going down with his ship in a gale off Cape Hatteras. The marriage did not take place until October 1859; and a son named for Commander Herndon died when only two. But another boy was born in

Mary Arthur McElroy: youngest sister of the President, ranking lady of the Arthur administration.

1864 and a girl, named for her mother, in 1871. Arthur's career brought the family an increasing prosperity; they decorated their home in the latest fashion and entertained prominent friends with elegance. At Christmas there were jewels from Tiffany for Nell, the finest toys for the children.

At the White House, Arthur would not give anyone the place that would have been his wife's. He asked his sister Mary (Mrs. John E. McElroy) to assume certain social duties and help care for his daughter. He presented a stained-glass window to St. John's Church in his wife's memory; it depicted angels of the Resurrection, and at his special request it was placed in the south transept so that he could see it at night from the White House with the lights of the church shining through.

Frances Folsom Cleveland
1864-1947

"I detest him so much that I don't even think his wife is beautiful." So spoke one of President Grover Cleveland's political foes—the only person, it seems, to deny the loveliness of this notable First Lady, first bride of a President to be married in the White House.

She was born in Buffalo, New York, only child of Emma C. Harmon and Oscar Folsom—who became a law partner of Cleveland's. As a devoted family friend Cleveland bought "Frank" her first baby carriage. As administrator of the Folsom estate after his partner's death, though never her legal guardian, he guided her education with sound advice. When she entered Wells College, he asked Mrs. Folsom's permission to correspond with her, and he kept her room bright with flowers.

Though Frank and her mother missed his inauguration in 1885, they visited him at the White House that spring. There affection turned into romance—despite 27 years' difference in age—and there the wedding took place on June 2, 1886.

Cleveland's scholarly sister Rose gladly gave up the duties of hostess for her own career in education; and with a bride as First Lady, state entertainments took on a new interest. Mrs. Cleveland's unaffected charm won her immediate popularity. She held two receptions a week—one on Saturday afternoons, when women with jobs were free to come.

Rose Elizabeth Cleveland: her bachelor brother's hostess in 15 months of his first term of office.

After the President's defeat in 1888, the Clevelands lived in New York City, where baby Ruth was born. With his unprecedented re-election, the First Lady returned to the White House as if she had been gone but a day. Through the political storms of this term she always kept her place in public favor. People took keen interest in the birth of Esther at the mansion in 1893, and of Marion in 1895. When the family left the White House, Mrs. Cleveland had become one of the most popular women ever to serve as hostess for the nation.

She bore two sons while the Clevelands lived in Princeton, New Jersey, and was at her husband's side when he died at their home, "Westland," in 1908.

In 1913 she married Thomas J. Preston, Jr., a professor of archeology, and remained a figure of note in the Princeton community until she died. She had reached her 84th year—nearly the age at which the venerable Mrs. Polk had welcomed her and her husband on a Presidential visit to the South, and chatted of changes in White House life from bygone days.

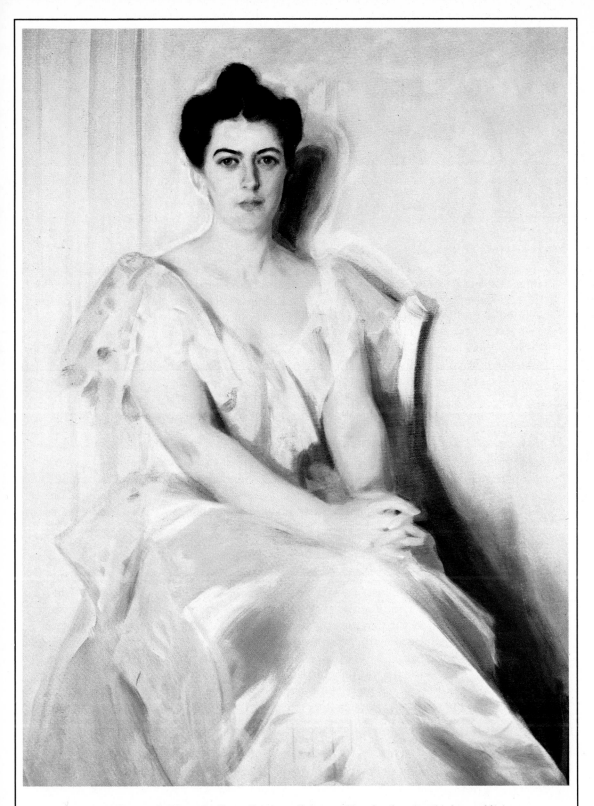

Youngest of First Ladies, Frances Folsom Cleveland stirred the public's sentimental admiration as a White House bride at 21 and earned nation-wide respect as a charming hostess, a loyal wife, and a capable mother. As President Cleveland expected, she proved "pretty level-headed." The fashionable Swedish portraitist Anders L. Zorn painted this study from life in 1899.

Caroline Lavinia Scott Harrison
1832-1892

The centennial of President Washington's inauguration heightened the nation's interest in its heroic past, and in 1890 Caroline Scott Harrison lent her prestige as First Lady to the founding of the National Society of the Daughters of the American Revolution. She served as its first President General. She took a special interest in the history of the White House, and the mature dignity with which she carried out her duties may overshadow the fun-loving nature that had charmed "Ben" Harrison when they met as teen-agers.

Born at Oxford, Ohio, in 1832, "Carrie" was the second daughter of Mary Potts Neal and the Reverend Dr. John W. Scott, a Presbyterian minister and founder of the Oxford Female Institute. As her father's pupil—brown-haired, petite, witty—she infatuated the reserved young Ben, then an honor student at Miami University; they were engaged before his graduation and married in 1853.

After early years of struggle while he established a law practice in Indianapolis, they enjoyed a happy family life interrupted only by the Civil War. Then, while General Harrison became a man of note in his profession, his wife cared for their son and daughter, gave active service to the First Presbyterian Church and to an orphans' home, and extended cordial hospitality to her many friends. Church views to the contrary, she saw no harm in private dancing lessons for her daughter—she liked dancing herself. Blessed with considerable artistic talent, she was an accomplished pianist; she especially enjoyed painting for recreation.

Illness repeatedly kept her away from Washington's winter social season during her husband's term in the Senate, 1881-1887, and she welcomed their return to private life; but she moved with poise to the White House in 1889 to continue the gracious way of life she had always created in her own home.

During the administration the Harrisons' daughter, Mary Harrison McKee, her two children, and other relatives lived at the White House. The First Lady tried in vain to have the overcrowded mansion enlarged but managed to assure an extensive renovation with up-to-date improvements. She established the collection of china associated with White House history. She worked for local charities as well. With other ladies of progressive views, she helped raise funds for the Johns Hopkins University medical school on condition that it admit women. She gave elegant receptions and dinners. In the winter of 1891-1892, however, she had to battle illness as she tried to fulfill her social obligations. She died of tuberculosis at the White House in October 1892, and after services in the East Room was buried from her own church in Indianapolis.

When official mourning ended, Mrs. McKee acted as hostess for her father in the last months of his term. (In 1896 he married his first wife's widowed niece and former secretary, Mary Scott Lord Dimmick; she survived him by nearly 47 years, dying in January 1948.)

To honor the memory of their first President General, Caroline Harrison, the Daughters of the American Revolution commissioned this posthumous portrait by Daniel Huntington and presented it to the White House in 1894.

Ida Saxton McKinley
1847-1907

There was little resemblance between the vivacious young woman who married William McKinley in January 1871 — a slender bride with sky-blue eyes and fair skin and masses of auburn hair—and the petulant invalid who moved into the White House with him in March 1897. Now her face was pallid and drawn, her close-cropped hair gray; her eyes were glazed with pain or dulled with sedative. Only one thing had remained the same: love which had brightened early years of happiness and endured through more than twenty years of illness.

Ida had been born in Canton, Ohio, in 1847, elder daughter of a socially prominent and well-to-do family. James A. Saxton, a banker, was indulgent to his two daughters. He educated them well in local schools and a finishing school, and then sent them to Europe on the grand tour.

Being pretty, fashionable, and a leader of the younger set in Canton did not satisfy Ida, so her broadminded father suggested that she work in his bank. As a cashier she caught the attention of Maj. William McKinley, who had come to Canton in 1867 to establish a law practice, and they fell deeply in love. While he advanced in his profession, his young wife devoted her time to home and husband. A daughter, Katherine, was born on Christmas Day, 1871; a second, in April 1873. This time Ida was seriously ill, and the frail baby died in August. Phlebitis and epileptic seizures shattered the mother's health; and even before little Katie died in 1876, she was a confirmed invalid.

As Congressman and then as governor of Ohio, William McKinley was never far from her side. He arranged their life to suit her convenience. She spent most of her waking hours in a small Victorian rocking chair that she had had since childhood; she sat doing fancywork and crocheting bedroom slippers while she waited for her husband, who indulged her every whim.

At the White House, the McKinleys acted as if her health were no great handicap to her role as First Lady. Richly and prettily dressed, she received guests at formal receptions seated in a blue velvet chair. She held a fragrant bouquet to suggest that she would not shake hands. Contrary to protocol, she was seated beside the President at state dinners and he, as always, kept close watch for signs of an impending seizure. If necessary, he would cover her face with a large handkerchief for a moment. The First Lady and her devoted husband seemed oblivious to any social inadequacy. Guests were discreet and newspapers silent on the subject of her "fainting spells." Only in recent years have the facts of her health been revealed.

When the President was shot by an assassin in September 1901, after his second inauguration, he thought primarily of her. He murmured to his secretary: "My wife— be careful, Cortelyou, how you tell her—oh, be careful." After his death she lived in Canton, cared for by her younger sister, visiting her husband's grave almost daily. She died in 1907, and lies entombed beside the President and near their two little daughters in Canton's McKinley Memorial Mausoleum.

Both Ida McKinley and her devoted husband posed in the private quarters of the White House for water-color miniatures by Emily Drayton Taylor in April 1899. Despite varied illnesses including epilepsy, she took up the role of First Lady with an indomitable determination.

With assured, cultivated taste, Edith Roosevelt approved decor for a renovated White House in 1902; she decided that the new ground-floor corridor, entryway for guests on important occasions, should display likenesses of "all the ladies . . . including myself." That same year Theobald Chartran had painted her confidently posed in the South Grounds. Her firmness and prudent advice earned the deep respect of her exuberant husband, and all who knew her. Ever since her day, the corridor has served as a gallery for portraits of recent First Ladies.

Edith Kermit Carow Roosevelt
1861-1948

Edith Kermit Carow knew Theodore Roosevelt from infancy; as a toddler she became a playmate of his younger sister Corinne. Born in Connecticut in 1861, daughter of Charles and Gertrude Tyler Carow, she grew up in an old New York brownstone on Union Square — an environment of comfort and tradition. Throughout childhood she and "Teedie" were in and out of each other's houses.

Attending Miss Comstock's school, she acquired the proper finishing touch for a young lady of that era. A quiet girl who loved books, she was often Theodore's companion for summer outings at Oyster Bay, Long Island; but this ended when he entered Harvard. Although she attended his wedding to Alice Hathaway Lee in 1880, their lives ran separately until 1885, when he was a young widower with an infant daughter, Alice.

Putting tragedy behind him, he and Edith were married in London in December, 1886. They settled down in a house on Sagamore Hill, at Oyster Bay, headquarters for a family that added five children in ten years: Theodore, Kermit, Ethel, Archibald, and Quentin. Throughout Roosevelt's intensely active career, family life remained close and entirely delightful. A small son remarked one day, "When Mother was a little girl, she must have been a boy!"

Public tragedy brought them into the White House, eleven days after President McKinley succumbed to an assassin's bullet. Assuming her new duties with characteristic dignity, Mrs. Roosevelt meant to guard the privacy of a family that attracted everyone's interest, and she tried to keep reporters outside her domain. The public, in consequence, heard little of the vigor of her character, her sound judgment, her efficient household management.

But in this administration the White House was unmistakably the social center of the land. Beyond the formal occasions, smaller parties brought together distinguished men and women from varied walks of life. Two family events were highlights: the wedding of "Princess Alice" to Nicholas Longworth, and Ethel's debut. A perceptive aide described the First Lady as "always the gentle, high-bred hostess; smiling often at what went on about her, yet never critical of the ignorant and tolerant always of the little insincerities of political life."

T.R. once wrote to Ted Jr. that "if Mother had been a mere unhealthy Patient Griselda I might have grown set in selfish and inconsiderate ways." She continued, with keen humor and unfailing dignity, to balance her husband's exuberance after they retired in 1909.

After his death in 1919, she traveled widely abroad but always returned to Sagamore Hill as her home. Alone much of the time, she never appeared lonely, being still an avid reader — "not only cultured but scholarly," as T.R. had said. She kept till the end her interest in the Needlework Guild, a charity which provided garments for the poor, and in the work of Christ Church at Oyster Bay. She died on September 30, 1948, at the age of 87.

Helen Herron Taft
1861-1943

As "the only unusual incident" of her girlhood, "Nellie" Herron Taft recalled her visit to the White House at 17 as the guest of President and Mrs. Hayes, intimate friends of her parents. Fourth child of Harriet Collins and John W. Herron, born in 1861, she had grown up in Cincinnati, Ohio, attending a private school in the city and studying music with enthusiasm.

The year after this notable visit she met "that adorable Will Taft," a tall young lawyer, at a sledding party. They found intellectual interests in common; friendship matured into love; Helen Herron and William Howard Taft were married in 1886. A "treasure," he called her, "self-contained, independent, and of unusual application." He wondered if they would ever reach Washington "in any official capacity" and suggested to her that they might—when she became Secretary of the Treasury!

No woman could hope for such a career in that day, but Mrs. Taft welcomed each step in her husband's: state judge, Solicitor General of the United States, federal circuit judge. In 1900 he agreed to take charge of American civil government in the Philippines. By now the children numbered three: Robert, Helen, and Charles. The delight with which she undertook the journey, and her willingness to take her children to a country still unsettled by war, were characteristic of this woman who loved a challenge. In Manila she handled a difficult role with enthusiasm and tact; she relished travel to Japan and China, and a special diplomatic mission to the Vatican.

Further travel with her husband, who became Secretary of War in 1904, brought a widened interest in world politics and a cosmopolitan circle of friends. His election to the Presidency in 1908 gave her a position she had long desired.

As First Lady, she still took an interest in politics but concentrated on giving the administration a particular social brilliance. Only two months after the inauguration she suffered a severe stroke. An indomitable will had her back in command again within a year. At the New Year's reception for 1910, she appeared in white crepe embroidered with gold—a graceful figure. Her daughter left college for a year to take part in social life at the White House, and the gaiety of Helen's debut enhanced the 1910 Christmas season.

During four years famous for social events, the most outstanding was an evening garden party for several thousand guests on the Tafts' silver wedding anniversary, June 19, 1911. Mrs. Taft remembered this as "the greatest event" in her White House experience. Her own book, *Recollections of Full Years,* gives her account of a varied life. And the capital's famous Japanese cherry trees, planted around the Tidal Basin at her request, form a notable memorial.

Her public role in Washington did not end when she left the White House. In 1921 her husband was appointed Chief Justice of the United States—the position he had desired most of all—and she continued to live in the capital after his death in 1930. Retaining to the end her love of travel and of classical music, she died at her home on May 22, 1943.

"My dearest and best critic," William Howard Taft *wrote of his wife. She wore her inaugural gown and a tiara to sit for Bror Kronstrand in 1910 at her New England summer home; the artist added a White House setting.*

Ellen Louise Axson Wilson
1860-1914

"I am naturally the most unambitious of women and life in the White House has no attractions for me." Mrs. Wilson was writing to thank President Taft for advice concerning the mansion he was leaving. Two years as first lady of New Jersey had given her valuable experience in the duties of a woman whose time belongs to the people. But though she always played a public role with dignity and grace, she never learned to enjoy it.

Those who knew her in the White House described her as calm and sweet, a motherly woman, pretty and refined. Her soft Southern voice had kept its slow drawl through many changes of residence.

Ellen Louise Axson grew up in Rome, Georgia, where her father, the Reverend S. E. Axson, was Presbyterian minister. "Tommy" Wilson first saw her when he was about six and she only a baby. In 1883, a young lawyer from Atlanta, he visited Rome and met "Miss Ellie Lou" again: a beautiful girl now, keeping house for a bereaved father. He thought, "what splendid laughing eyes!" Despite their instant attraction they did not marry until 1885—she was unwilling to leave her heartbroken father.

When Bryn Mawr College offered the young historian $1,500 a year, he and his bride could live near the campus and have her little brother with them. Humorously insisting that her own children must not be born Yankees, she went to relatives in Georgia for the birth of Margaret in 1886 and Jessie in 1887. But Eleanor was born in Connecticut, while Wilson was teaching at Wesleyan University. His distinguished career at Princeton began in 1890, bringing his wife new social responsibilities.

From such demands she took refuge, as always, in art. She had studied briefly in New York, and the quality of her paintings compares favorably with other amateur work of the period. She had a studio with a skylight installed at the White House in 1913, and found time for painting despite the weddings of two daughters within six months and the duties of hostess for the nation.

The Wilsons had preferred to begin the administration without an inaugural ball, and the First Lady's entertainments were simple; but her unaffected cordiality made her parties successful. In their first year she convinced her scrupulous husband that it would be perfectly proper to invite influential legislators to a private dinner, and when such an evening led to agreement on a tariff bill, he told a friend, "You see what a wise wife I have!"

Descendant of slaveowners, Ellen Wilson lent her prestige to the cause of improving housing in the capital's Negro slums. Visiting dilapidated alleys, she brought them to the attention of debutantes and Congressmen. Her death spurred passage of a remedial bill she had worked for. Her health failing slowly from Bright's disease, she died serenely on August 6, 1914. On the day before her death, she made her physician promise to tell Wilson "later" that she hoped he would marry again; she murmured at the end, ". . . take good care of my husband." Struggling grimly to control his grief, Wilson took her to Rome for burial among her kin.

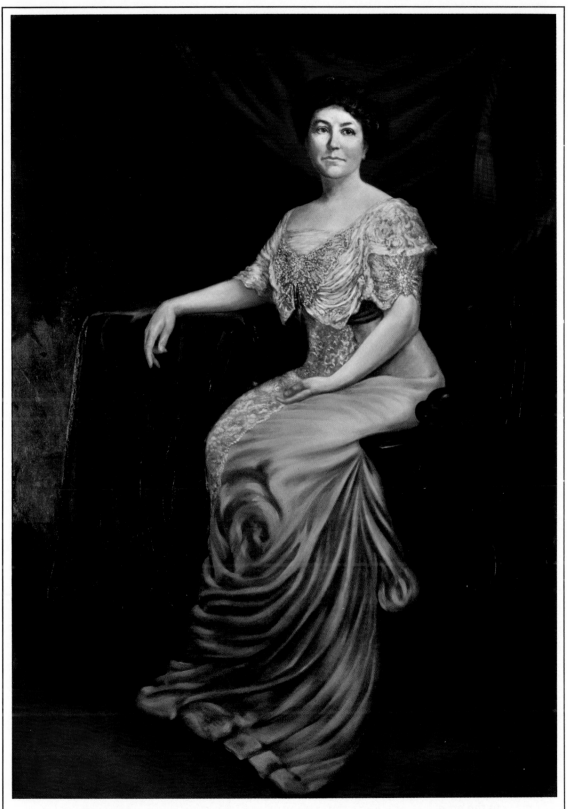

First wife of Woodrow Wilson, Ellen Louise Axson shared his life from his teaching days at Bryn Mawr to the Presidency. In Washington she devoted much time to humanitarian causes—education for mountain children, better housing for Negroes. Painter and date of this portrait remain unknown.

Solace and support for a troubled President, Edith Wilson saw him through the agonies of wartime, frustrations of protracted peace negotiations, rejection of his dream for world order, illness, and death. Adolpho Muller-Ury portrayed her soon after she had entered the White House, early in 1916.

Edith Bolling Galt Wilson
1872-1961

"Secret President," "first woman to run the government"—so legend has labeled a First Lady whose role gained unusual significance when her husband suffered prolonged and disabling illness. A happy, protected childhood and first marriage had prepared Edith Wilson for the duties of helpmate and hostess; widowhood had taught her something of business matters.

Descendant of Virginia aristocracy, she was born in Wytheville in 1872, seventh among eleven children of Sallie White and Judge William Holcombe Bolling. Until the age of 12 she never left the town; at 15 she went to Martha Washington College to study music, with a second year at a smaller school in Richmond.

Visiting a married sister in Washington, pretty young Edith met a businessman named Norman Galt; in 1896 they were married. For 12 years she lived as a contented (though childless) young matron in the capital, with vacations abroad. In 1908 her husband died unexpectedly. Shrewdly, Edith Galt chose a good manager who operated the family's jewelry firm with financial success.

By a quirk of fate and a chain of friendships, Mrs. Galt met the bereaved President, still mourning profoundly for his first wife. A man who depended on feminine companionship, the lonely Wilson took an instant liking to Mrs. Galt, charming and intelligent and unusually pretty. Admiration changed swiftly to love. In proposing to her, he made the poignant statement that "in this place time is not measured by weeks, or months, or years, but by deep human experiences...." They were married privately on December 18, 1915, at her home; and after they returned from a brief honeymoon in Virginia, their happiness made a vivid impression on their friends and White House staff.

Though the new First Lady had sound qualifications for the role of hostess, the social aspect of the administration was overshadowed by the war in Europe and abandoned after the United States entered the conflict in 1917. Edith Wilson submerged her own life in her husband's, trying to keep him fit under tremendous strain. She accompanied him to Europe when the Allies conferred on terms of peace.

Wilson returned to campaign for Senate approval of the peace treaty and the League of Nations Covenant. His health failed in September 1919; a stroke left him partly paralyzed. His constant attendant, Mrs. Wilson took over many routine duties and details of government. But she did not initiate programs or make major decisions, and she did not try to control the executive branch. She selected matters for her husband's attention and let everything else go to the heads of departments or remain in abeyance. Her "stewardship," she called this. And in *My Memoir*, published in 1939, she stated emphatically that her husband's doctors had urged this course upon her.

In 1921, the Wilsons retired to a comfortable home in Washington, where he died three years later. A highly respected figure in the society of the capital, Mrs. Wilson lived on to ride in President Kennedy's inaugural parade. She died later in 1961: on December 28, the anniversary of her famous husband's birth.

Florence Kling Harding
1860-1924

Daughter of the richest man in a small town—Amos Kling, the local banker—Florence Mabel Kling was born in Marion, Ohio, in 1860, to grow up in a setting of wealth, position, and privilege. Much like her strong-willed father in temperament, she developed a self-reliance rare in girls of that era.

A music course at the Cincinnati Conservatory completed her education. When only 19, she eloped with Henry De Wolfe, a neighbor two years her senior. He proved a spendthrift and a heavy drinker who soon deserted her, so she returned to Marion with her baby son. Refusing to live at home, she rented rooms and earned her own money by giving piano lessons to children of the neighborhood. She divorced De Wolfe in 1886 and resumed her maiden name; he died at age 35.

Warren G. Harding had come to Marion when only 16 and, showing a flair for newspaper work, had managed to buy the little *Daily Star*. When he met Florence a courtship quickly developed. Over Amos Kling's angry opposition they were married in 1891, in a house that Harding had planned, and this remained their home for the rest of their lives. (They had no children.)

Mrs. Harding soon took over the *Star*'s circulation department, spanking newsboys when necessary. "No pennies escaped her," a friend recalled, and the paper prospered while its owner's political success increased. As he rose through Ohio politics and became a United States Senator, his wife directed all her acumen to his career. He became Republican nominee for President in 1920 and "the Duchess," as he called her, worked tirelessly for his election. In her own words: "I have only one real hobby—my husband."

She had never been a guest at the White House; and former President Taft, meeting the President-elect and Mrs. Harding, discussed its social customs with her and stressed the value of ceremony. Writing to Nellie, he concluded that the new First Lady was "a nice woman" and would "readily adapt herself."

When Mrs. Harding moved into the White House, she opened mansion and grounds to the public again—both had been closed throughout President Wilson's illness. She herself suffered from a chronic kidney ailment, but she threw herself into the job of First Lady with energy and willpower. Garden parties for veterans were regular events on a crowded social calendar. The President and his wife relaxed at poker parties in the White House library, where liquor was available although the Eighteenth Amendment made it illegal.

Mrs. Harding always liked to travel with her husband. She was with him in the summer of 1923 when he died unexpectedly in California, shortly before the public learned of the major scandals facing his administration.

With astonishing fortitude she endured the long train ride to Washington with the President's body, the state funeral at the Capitol, the last service and burial at Marion. She died in Marion on November 21, 1924, surviving Warren Harding by little more than a year of illness and sorrow.

"The Duchess," her husband called Florence Harding. Her drive and determination helped put the 29th President in the White House in 1921. There,
in the Queens' Bedroom, hangs this portrait from life by Philip de László.

Grace Anna Goodhue Coolidge
1879-1957

For her "fine personal influence exerted as First Lady of the Land," Grace Coolidge received a gold medal from the National Institute of Social Sciences. In 1931 she was voted one of America's twelve greatest living women.

She had grown up in the Green Mountain city of Burlington, Vermont, only child of Andrew and Lemira B. Goodhue, born in 1879. While still a girl she heard of a school for deaf children in Northampton, Massachusetts, and eventually decided to share its challenging work. She graduated from the University of Vermont in 1902 and went to teach at the Clarke School for the Deaf that autumn.

In Northampton she met Calvin Coolidge; they belonged to the same boating, picnicking, whist-club set, composed largely of members of the local Congregational Church. In October 1905 they were married at her parents' home. They lived modestly; they moved into half of a duplex two weeks before their first son was born, and she budgeted expenses well within the income of a struggling small-town lawyer.

To Grace Coolidge may be credited a full share in her husband's rise in politics. She worked hard, kept up appearances, took her part in town activities, attended her church, and offset his shyness with a gay friendliness. She bore a second son in 1908, and it was she who played backyard baseball with the boys. As Coolidge was rising to the rank of governor, the family kept the duplex; he rented a dollar-and-a-half room in Boston and came home on weekends.

In 1921, as wife of the Vice President, Grace Coolidge went from her housewife's routine into Washington society and quickly became the most popular woman in the capital. Her zest for life and her innate simplicity charmed even the most critical. Stylish clothes—a frugal husband's one indulgence—set off her good looks.

After Harding's death, she planned the new administration's social life as her husband wanted it: unpretentious but dignified. Her time and her friendliness now belonged to the nation, and she was generous with both. As she wrote later, she was "I, and yet, not I—this was the wife of the President of the United States and she took precedence over me. . . ." Under the sorrow of her younger son's sudden death at 16, she never let grief interfere with her duties as First Lady. Tact and gaiety made her one of the most popular hostesses of the White House, and she left Washington in 1929 with the country's respect and love.

For greater privacy in Northampton, the Coolidges bought "The Beeches," a large house with spacious grounds. Calvin Coolidge died there in 1933. He had summed up their marriage in his *Autobiography:* "For almost a quarter of a century she has borne with my infirmities, and I have rejoiced in her graces." After his death she sold The Beeches, bought a smaller house, and in time undertook new ventures she had longed to try: her first airplane ride, her first trip to Europe. She kept her aversion to publicity and her sense of fun until her death in 1957. Her chief activity as she grew older was serving as a trustee of the Clarke School; her great pleasure was the family of her surviving son, John.

First as a Vice President's wife, then as First Lady, Grace Goodhue Coolidge brought to Washington society the charm and simplicity of her New England upbringing and her love of people, outdoor activity, and animals. Howard Chandler Christy portrayed her in 1924 with her famous collie Rob Roy.

Lou Henry Hoover
1874-1944

Admirably equipped to preside at the White House, Lou Henry Hoover brought to it long experience as wife of a man eminent in public affairs at home and abroad. She had shared his interests since they met in a geology lab at Leland Stanford University. She was a freshman, he a senior, and he was fascinated, as he declared later, "by her whimsical mind, her blue eyes and a broad grinnish smile."

Born in Iowa, in 1874, she grew up there for ten years. Then her father, Charles D. Henry, decided that the climate of southern California would favor the health of his wife, Florence. He took his daughter on camping trips in the hills—her greatest pleasures in her early teens. Lou became a fine horsewoman; she hunted, and preserved specimens with the skill of a taxidermist; she developed an enthusiasm for rocks, minerals, and mining. She entered Stanford in 1894—"slim and supple as a reed," a classmate recalled, with a "wealth of brown hair"—and completed her course before marrying Herbert Hoover in 1899.

The newlyweds left at once for China, where he won quick recognition as a mining engineer. His career took them about the globe—Ceylon, Burma, Siberia, Australia, Egypt, Japan, Europe—while her talent for home-making eased their time in a dozen foreign lands. Two sons, Herbert and Allan, were born during this adventurous life, which made their father a youthful millionaire.

During World War I, while Hoover earned world fame administering emergency relief programs, she was often with him but spent some time with the boys in California. In 1919 she saw construction begin for a long-planned home in Palo Alto. In 1921, however, his appointment as Secretary of Commerce took the family to Washington. There she spent eight years busy with the social duties of a Cabinet wife and an active participation in the Girl Scout movement, including service as its president.

Taking charge at the White House in 1929, the Hoovers abolished the old New Year's reception—by now an assembly line of thousands—but whenever possible the First Lady welcomed the public with poise and dignity. She took part in varied ceremonies, such as christening ships, and substituted for her husband in others, making speeches for him to spare him time for work. Her restoration of Lincoln's study for his use pleased him greatly. She paid with her own money the cost of reproducing furniture owned by Monroe, for a period sitting room. She dressed handsomely; a secretary at the mansion thought she "never fitted more perfectly into the White House picture than in her formal evening gown." Her social events remained notably elegant—the Hoovers used their own private funds for entertaining while the country suffered from a worsening economic depression.

In 1933 they retired to Palo Alto, but maintained an apartment in New York. Mr. Hoover learned the full lavishness of his wife's charities only after her death there on January 7, 1944; she had helped the education, he said, "of a multitude of boys and girls." In retrospect he stated her ideal for the position she had held: "a symbol of everything wholesome in American life."

Perfectionist of hospitality, Lou Hoover as First Lady considered formal entertaining a duty to the American people. For the White House Collection, Richard M. Brown copied a 1932 portrait from life by Philip de László.

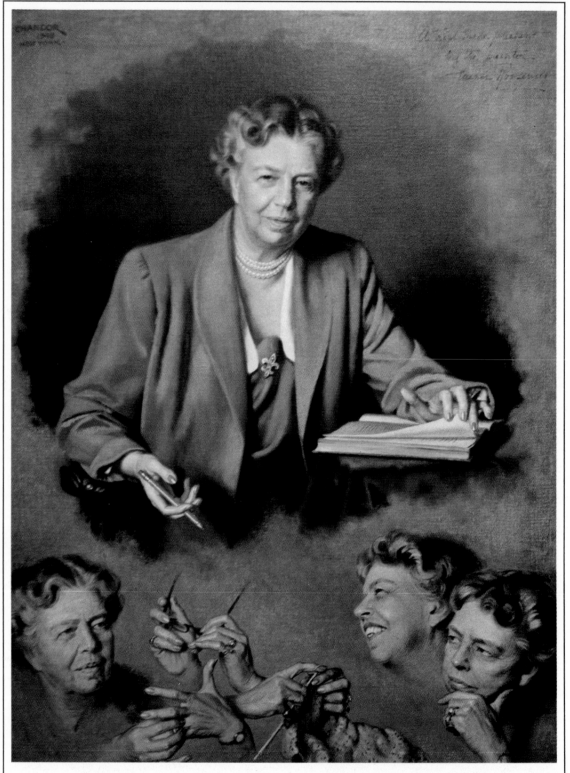

Douglas Chandor's portrait of Eleanor Roosevelt at age 65 captures a range of moods and suggests her astonishing energy. She devoted a long career to victims of poverty, prejudice, and war. Painfully shy and self-conscious in her youth, often a controversial figure in the role of President's wife, she won international respect in later years as "First Lady of the World."

Anna Eleanor Roosevelt Roosevelt
1884-1962

A shy, awkward child, starved for recognition and love, Eleanor Roosevelt grew into a woman with great sensitivity to the underprivileged of all creeds, races, and nations. Her constant work to improve their lot made her one of the most loved — and for some years one of the most reviled — women of her generation.

She was born in New York City on October 11, 1884, daughter of lovely Anna Hall and Elliott Roosevelt, younger brother of Theodore. When her mother died in 1892, the children went to live with Grandmother Hall; her adored father died only two years later. Attending a distinguished school in England gave her, at 15, her first chance to develop self-confidence among other girls.

Tall, slender, graceful of figure but apprehensive at the thought of being a wallflower, she returned for a debut that she dreaded. In her circle of friends was a distant cousin, handsome young Franklin Delano Roosevelt. They became engaged in 1903 and were married in 1905, with her uncle the President giving the bride away. Within eleven years Eleanor bore six children; one son died in infancy. "I suppose I was fitting pretty well into the pattern of a fairly conventional, quiet, young society matron," she wrote later in her autobiography.

In Albany, where Franklin served in the state Senate from 1910 to 1913, Eleanor started her long career as political helpmate. She gained a knowledge of Washington and its ways while he served as Assistant Secretary of the Navy. When he was stricken with poliomyelitis in 1921, she tended him devotedly. She became active in the women's division of the State Democratic Committee to keep his interest in politics alive. From his successful campaign for governor in 1928 to the day of his death, she dedicated her life to his purposes. She became eyes and ears for him, a trusted and tireless reporter.

When Mrs. Roosevelt came to the White House in 1933, she understood social conditions better than any of her predecessors and she transformed the role of First Lady accordingly. She never shirked official entertaining; she greeted thousands with charming friendliness. She also broke precedent to hold press conferences, travel to all parts of the country, give lectures and radio broadcasts, and express her opinions candidly in a daily syndicated newspaper column, "My Day."

This made her a tempting target for political enemies but her integrity, her graciousness, and her sincerity of purpose endeared her personally to many — from heads of state to servicemen she visited abroad during World War II. As she had written wistfully at 14: ". . . no matter how plain a woman may be if truth & loyalty are stamped upon her face all will be attracted to her. . . ."

After the President's death in 1945 she returned to a cottage at his Hyde Park estate; she told reporters: "the story is over." Within a year, however, she began her service as American spokesman in the United Nations. She continued a vigorous career until her strength began to wane in 1962. She died in New York City that November, and was buried at Hyde Park beside her husband.

Elizabeth Virginia Wallace Truman
1885-

Whistle-stopping in 1948, President Harry Truman often ended his campaign talk by introducing his wife as "the Boss" and his daughter, Margaret, as "the Boss's Boss," and they smiled and waved as the train picked up steam. The sight of that close-knit family gallantly fighting against such long odds had much to do with his surprise victory at the polls that November.

Strong family ties in the southern tradition had always been important around Independence, Missouri, where a baby girl was born to Margaret ("Madge") Gates and David Wallace on February 13, 1885. Christened Elizabeth Virginia, she grew up as "Bess." Harry Truman, whose family moved to town in 1890, always kept his first impression of her—"golden curls" and "the most beautiful blue eyes." A relative said, "there never was but one girl in the world" for him. They attended the same schools from fifth grade through high school.

In recent years their daughter has written a vivid sketch of Bess as a girl: "a marvelous athlete—the best third baseman in Independence, a superb tennis player, a tireless ice skater—and she was pretty besides." She also had many "strong opinions. . . . and no hesitation about stating them Missouri style—straight from the shoulder."

For Bess and Harry, World War I altered a deliberate courtship. He proposed and they became engaged before Lieutenant Truman left for the battlefields of France in 1918. They were married in June 1919; they lived in Mrs. Wallace's home, where Mary Margaret was born in 1924.

When Harry Truman became active in politics, Mrs. Truman traveled with him and shared his platform appearances as the public had come to expect a candidate's wife to do. His election to the Senate in 1934 took the family to Washington. Reluctant to be a public figure herself, she always shared his thoughts and interests in private. When she joined his office staff as a secretary, he said, she earned "every cent I pay her." His wartime role as chairman of a special committee on defense spending earned him national recognition—and a place on the Democratic ticket as President Roosevelt's fourth-term running mate. Three months after their inauguration Roosevelt was dead. On April 12, 1945, Harry Truman took the President's oath of office— and Bess, who managed to look on with composure, was the new First Lady.

In the White House, its lack of privacy was distasteful to her. As her husband put it later, she was "not especially interested" in the "formalities and pomp or the artificiality which, as we had learned . . . , inevitably surround the family of the President." Though she conscientiously fulfilled the social obligations of her position, she did only what was necessary. While the mansion was rebuilt during the second term, the Trumans lived in Blair House and kept social life to a minimum.

They returned to Independence in 1953. There Mrs. Truman happily devoted her time to friends and family. Since her husband's death in December 1972, she has continued to live in the family home. Her chief enjoyments have been visits from Margaret with her husband, Clifton Daniel, and their four sons.

Dignified and witty Bess Truman keeps the original painting of this White House replica in her Missouri home. Her daughter, Margaret Truman Daniel, calls her "a warmhearted, kind lady, with a robust sense of humor."

Mamie Geneva Doud Eisenhower
1896-

Mamie Eisenhower's bangs and sparkling blue eyes were as much trademarks of an administration as the President's famous grin. Her outgoing manner, her feminine love of pretty clothes and jewelry, and her obvious pride in husband and home, made her a very popular First Lady.

Born Mamie Geneva Doud in Boone, Iowa, she moved with her family to Colorado when she was seven and her father, John Sheldon Doud, retired from business. In 1906 he bought a home in Denver, but he found that in winter his family was more comfortable in the milder climate of San Antonio, Texas.

There, in 1915, at Fort Sam Houston, Mamie met Dwight D. Eisenhower, a young second lieutenant on his first tour of duty. She drew his attention instantly, he recalled: "a vivacious and attractive girl, smaller than average, saucy in the look about her face and in her whole attitude." On St. Valentine's Day in 1916 he gave her a miniature of his West Point class ring to seal a formal engagement; they were married at the Doud home in Denver on July 1.

For years Mamie Eisenhower's life followed the pattern of other Army wives': a succession of posts in the United States, in the Panama Canal Zone; duty in France, in the Philippines. She once estimated that in 37 years she had unpacked her household at least 27 times. Each move meant another step up the career ladder for her husband, with increasing responsibilities for her.

Their first son, Doud Dwight or "Icky," who was born in 1917, died of scarlet fever in 1921—a loss still mourned by his mother. A second child, John, was born in 1922, at Denver. He also made a career in the Army; and he and his family have been his mother's delight and mainstay.

During World War II, while promotion and fame came to "Ike," his wife lived in an apartment in Washington. After he became president of Columbia University in 1948, the Eisenhowers purchased a farm at Gettysburg, Pennsylvania: the first home they had ever owned. Then his service as commander of North Atlantic Treaty Organization forces—and hers as his hostess at a chateau near Paris—interrupted the work on their dream home, finally completed as she planned it in 1955. They celebrated with a housewarming picnic for domestic and political staff (and spouses) from their last temporary quarters: the White House.

When Eisenhower had campaigned for President, his wife had cheerfully shared his travels; when he was inaugurated in 1953, the American people warmly welcomed her as First Lady. Diplomacy—and air travel—in the postwar world brought changes in their official hospitality. The Eisenhowers entertained an unprecedented number of heads of state and leaders of foreign governments, and Mamie's evident enjoyment of her role endeared her to her guests and to the public.

In 1961 the Eisenhowers returned to Gettysburg for eight years of contented retirement together. Since his death in 1969, she has continued to live there, devoting even more of her time to her family and to friends.

Her famed and favorite pink casts a soft glow from Mrs. Eisenhower's rhinestone-studded inaugural gown. After many separations in Army life, she and the President happily resided in the White House for eight years.

Jacqueline Kennedy, portrayed by Aaron Shikler in 1970, stirred national interest in obtaining antiques and works of art for the White House. She planned the first historical guidebook of the mansion for its many visitors.

Jacqueline Lee Bouvier Kennedy
1929-

The inauguration of John F. Kennedy in 1961 brought to the White House and to the heart of the nation a beautiful young wife and the first young children of a President since the days of Grover Cleveland or Theodore Roosevelt. Jacqueline Kennedy not only looked like a fairy-tale princess, her family background had permitted her to be reared like one.

She was born Jacqueline Lee Bouvier, daughter of John Vernon Bouvier III and his wife, Janet Lee. Her early years were divided between New York City and East Hampton, Long Island, where she learned to ride almost as soon as she could walk. She was educated at the best of private schools; she wrote poems and stories, drew illustrations for them, and studied ballet.

Her mother, who had obtained a divorce, married Hugh D. Auchincloss in 1942 and brought her two girls to "Merrywood," his home near Washington, D. C., with summers spent at his estate in Newport, Rhode Island. Jacqueline was dubbed "the Debutante of the year" for the 1947-1948 season, but her social success did not keep her from continuing her education. As a Vassar student she traveled extensively, and she spent her junior year in France. These experiences left her with a great empathy for people of foreign countries, especially the French.

Back in Washington, with a job as "inquiring photographer" for a local newspaper, her path soon crossed that of Senator Kennedy, who had the reputation of being the most eligible bachelor in the capital. Their romance progressed slowly and privately, but their wedding at Newport in 1953 attracted nationwide publicity as a grand extravaganza.

With marriage "Jackie" had to adapt herself to the new role of wife to one of the country's most energetic political figures. Her own public appearances were highly successful, but limited in number. After the sadness of a miscarriage and a stillbirth, Caroline Bouvier was born in 1957; John Jr. was born between the election of 1960 and Inauguration Day. Patrick Bouvier, born prematurely on August 7, 1963, died two days later.

To the role of First Lady, Jacqueline Kennedy brought beauty, intelligence, and cultivated taste. Her interest in the arts, publicized by press and television, inspired an attention to culture never before evident at a national level. She devoted much time and study to making the White House a museum of decorative arts and American history as well as a family residence of elegance and charm. But she defined her major role as "to take care of the President" and added that "if you bungle raising your children, I don't think whatever else you do well matters very much."

Mrs. Kennedy's gallant courage during the tragedy of her husband's assassination won her the admiration of the world. Thereafter it seemed the public would never allow her the privacy she desired for herself and her children. She moved to New York City; and in 1968 she married the wealthy Greek businessman Aristotle Onassis, 23 years her senior, who died in March 1975.

Claudia Taylor (Lady Bird) Johnson
1912-

Christened Claudia Alta Taylor when she was born in a country mansion near Karnack, Texas, she received her nickname "Lady Bird" as a small child; and as Lady Bird she is known and loved throughout America today. Perhaps that name was prophetic, as there has seldom been a First Lady so attuned to wildlife and the importance of conserving the environment.

Her mother, Minnie Pattillo Taylor, died when she was five, so she was reared by her father, her aunt, and family servants. From her father, Thomas Jefferson Taylor, who had prospered, she learned much about the business world. An excellent student, she also learned to love classical literature. At the University of Texas she earned bachelor's degrees in arts and in journalism.

In 1934 Lady Bird met Lyndon Baines Johnson, then a Congressional secretary visiting Austin on official business; he promptly asked her for a date, which she accepted. He courted her from Washington with letters, telegrams, and telephone calls. Seven weeks later he was back in Texas; he proposed to her and she accepted. In her own words: "Sometimes Lyndon simply takes your breath away." They were married in November 1934.

The years that followed were devoted to Lyndon's political career, with "Bird" as partner, confidante, and helpmate. She helped keep his Congressional office open during World War II when he volunteered for naval service; and in 1955, when he had a severe heart attack, she helped his staff keep things running smoothly until he could return to his post as Majority Leader of the Senate. He once remarked that voters "would happily have elected her over me."

After ten years of marriage, and repeated miscarriages, she gave birth to Lynda Bird (now Mrs. Charles S. Robb); Luci Baines (now Mrs. Patrick John Nugent) was born three years later.

In the election of 1960, Lady Bird covered 35,000 miles of campaign trail as an unmistakable asset for the Democratic candidates; and as wife of the Vice President she got her first taste of being one of America's ambassadors of good will. In less than three years she visited 33 foreign countries.

Moving to the White House after Kennedy's murder, she did her best to ease a painful transition. She soon set her own stamp of Texas hospitality on social events, but these were not her chief concern. She created a First Lady's Committee for a More Beautiful Capital, then expanded her program to include the entire nation. She took a highly active part in her husband's war-on-poverty program, especially the Head Start project for preschool children.

At the end of his term of office, the Johnsons returned to Texas, where he died in 1973. Her *White House Diary*, published in 1970, gives a sensitive and detailed view of her life as First Lady. Today she leads a busy life devoted to her husband's memory, her children and grandchildren, and causes dear to her—notably the University of Texas and the beautification of the land.

Flower- and wilderness-lover, Lady Bird Johnson sponsored a beautification project that came to include the nation's cities and highways. "A woman of great depth and excellent judgment," President Johnson described her.

While First Lady, Pat Nixon traveled over the world more than any of her predecessors, alone or with her husband. She encouraged volunteer work—"individual attention and love and concern"—to help the less fortunate.

Patricia Ryan Nixon
1912-

Born Thelma Catherine Ryan on March 16 in Ely, Nevada, "Pat" Nixon acquired her nickname within hours. Her father, William Ryan, called her his "St. Patrick's babe in the morn" when he came home from the mines before dawn.

Soon the family moved to California and settled on a small truck farm near Los Angeles—a life of hard work with few luxuries. Her mother, Kate Halberstadt Bender Ryan, died in 1925; at 13 Pat assumed all the household duties for her father and two older brothers. At 18, she lost her father after nursing him through months of serious illness. Left on her own and determined to continue her education, she worked her way through the University of Southern California. She held part-time jobs on campus, as a sales clerk in a fashionable department store, and as an extra in the movies —and she graduated cum laude in 1937.

She accepted a position as a high-school teacher in Whittier; and there she met Richard Nixon, who had come home from Duke University Law School to establish a practice. They became acquainted at a Little Theater group when they were cast in the same play, and were married on June 21, 1940.

During World War II, she worked as a government economist while he served in the Navy. She campaigned at his side in 1946 when he entered politics, running successfully for Congress, and afterward. Within six years she saw him elected to the House, the Senate, and the Vice Presidency on the ticket with Dwight D. Eisenhower. Despite the demands of official life, the Nixons were devoted parents to their two daughters, Tricia (now Mrs. Edward Cox), and Julie (Mrs. David Eisenhower).

A tireless campaigner when he ran unsuccessfully for President in 1960, she was at his side when he ran again in 1968—and won. She had once remarked succinctly, "It takes heart to be in political life."

A gracious hostess as First Lady, she used her position to encourage volunteer service—"the spirit of people helping people." She invited hundreds of families to nondenominational Sunday services in the East Room, unprecedented in White House history. She instituted a series of performances by artists in varied American traditions—from opera to bluegrass—and took pride in the number of fine antiques and significant paintings added to the White House Collection.

She had shared her husband's journeys abroad in the Vice Presidential years and continued this during his Presidency. Official travel took them to most of the nations of the world, including the historic visit to the People's Republic of China and the summit meeting in the Soviet Union. On her first solo trip, the First Lady made a journey of compassion to take relief supplies to earthquake victims in Peru. Later she visited Africa and South America with the unique diplomatic standing of Personal Representative of the President. Always she was a charming envoy for the nation.

Mrs. Nixon returned to California with her husband upon his resignation in 1974. She had met the troubled days of Watergate with dignity. She said simply, "I love my husband, I believe in him, and I am proud of his accomplishments."

Once a professional dancer with Martha Graham and a teacher of dance to underprivileged youngsters, Betty Ford continues her support of dance and encourages the other arts. She staunchly advocates women's rights as well.

Elizabeth Bloomer Ford
1918-

In 25 years of political life, Betty Bloomer Ford did not expect to become First Lady. As wife of Representative Gerald R. Ford, she looked forward to his retirement and more time together. In late 1973 his selection as Vice President was a surprise to her. She was just becoming accustomed to their new roles when he became President upon Mr. Nixon's resignation in August 1974.

Born Elizabeth Anne Bloomer in Chicago, she grew up in Grand Rapids, Michigan, and graduated from high school there. She studied modern dance at Bennington College in Vermont, decided to make it a career, and became a member of Martha Graham's noted concert group in New York City, supporting herself as a fashion model for the John Robert Powers firm.

Close ties with her family and her home town took her back to Grand Rapids, where she became fashion coordinator for a department store. She also organized her own dance group, and taught dance to handicapped children.

Her first marriage, at age 24, ended in divorce on the grounds of incompatibility five years later. Not long afterward she began dating Jerry Ford, football hero, graduate of the University of Michigan and Yale Law School, and soon a candidate for Congress. They were married during the 1948 campaign; he won his election; and the Fords lived in the Washington area for nearly three decades thereafter.

Their four children—Michael Gerald, John Gardner, Steven Meigs, and Susan Elizabeth—were born in the next ten years, and Betty Ford found herself having to shoulder much of the responsibility of bringing up the family because of her husband's involvement in politics. She supervised the home, did the cooking, undertook volunteer work, took part in the activities of "House wives" and "Senate wives" for Congressional and Republican clubs, and campaigned for her husband as well.

Betty Ford faced her new life as First Lady with dignity and serenity. She accepted it as a challenge, and in her own words, "I like challenges very much." Her experience in the business of fashion and as a professional dancer is apparent in the style of her wardrobe and the grace with which she walks. She has the self-confidence to express herself with humor and forthrightness whether she speaks to friends, to the press, or to a multitude.

Forced to undergo radical surgery for breast cancer on September 28, 1974, she reassured many troubled women by discussing her ordeal openly. She explained that "maybe if I as First Lady could talk about it candidly and without embarrassment, many other people would be able to as well." As soon as possible, she resumed her duties as hostess and public-spirited citizen. She did not hesitate to state her views on controversial issues such as the Equal Rights Amendment, which she strongly supports.

She has described her role as "much more of a 24-hour job than anyone would guess," and says of her predecessors: "now that I realize what they've had to put up with, I have new respect and admiration for every one of them."

Rosalynn Smith Carter
1927-

"She's the girl I want to marry," Jimmy Carter told his mother, Lillian Gordy Carter, after his first date with 17-year-old Rosalynn Smith.

Rosalynn, who had grown up as friend and neighbor of the Carter family in Plains, Georgia, was born there on August 18, 1927, to Allie Murray Smith and Edgar Smith. The first of four children, she grew up in a small-town atmosphere where strong family ties were the norm and dedication to church and community was expected. When she was only 13, her father died and her mother became a dressmaker in her home to help support the family. As the oldest, Rosalynn worked beside her mother helping with the sewing, the house, and the other children. The times were difficult, but Rosalynn completed high school and went on to Georgia Southwestern College at Americus. It was after her freshman year there in 1945 that she first dated midshipman Jimmy Carter, home from the Naval Academy at Annapolis, Maryland.

Their romance progressed, and after their graduations in 1946, they were married. They went to Norfolk, Virginia, where the young ensign began his naval career and Rosalynn Smith Carter started her career as a Navy wife. Assignments kept the couple on the move. All three of their sons were born in different places: John William in Portsmouth, Virginia; James Earl III in Honolulu, Hawaii; and Donnel Jeffrey in New London, Connecticut. With Jimmy Carter often away on sea duty, Mrs. Carter handled all the family matters. The Carters' only daughter, Amy Lynn, was born in Plains, Georgia, in 1967.

When Jimmy Carter's father died in 1953, the Carters left the service and returned to Plains to run the family peanut business. Mrs. Carter took over the accounts after her husband opened a fertilizer-and-seed business, and soon she was working full time. Then, in 1962, Jimmy Carter entered politics.

Ever since that first race, Rosalynn has been an important member of his political team. She helped her husband develop support for his successful campaign for Governor of Georgia. During the Presidential campaign, Rosalynn doubled the Carter political mileage by traveling independently in more than 40 states. In the final week she covered approximately 15,000 miles, winning votes with her quiet, friendly approach.

A skillful public speaker, Rosalynn Carter is a serious, hardworking First Lady who goes to her own office in the East Wing to concentrate on routine duties or special projects. She sustains the ever-lengthening tradition of White House hospitality. Moreover, she sometimes attends Cabinet meetings and high-level briefings. In 1977 she visited the leaders of seven Latin American countries as her husband's personal emissary. Since then she has filled this role repeatedly, both on ceremonial occasions and special missions. Her success with programs for the mentally ill and the elderly has encouraged her to expand her interests. She hopes to focus public attention on self-help and volunteer efforts to cope with community problems so that the best projects will become examples to be followed throughout the land.

For many years, Rosalynn Carter has taken an active interest in volunteer work and in helping the emotionally and mentally ill. During 1977-78 she served as the Honorary Chairperson of the President's Commission on Mental Health.

Illustrations Credits

Photographic portraits of Mrs. Nixon
and Mrs. Carter will appear until official
paintings have been acquired.

Composition for *The First Ladies* by National
Geographic's Phototypographic Division, Carl M.
Shrader, Chief; Lawrence F. Ludwig, Assistant
Chief. Printed and bound by Fawcett Printing
Corp., Rockville, Md. Color separations by
Colorgraphics, Inc., Forestville, Md.

Host and hostess of the White House, the President and First Lady Frances Cleveland welcome officers of the armed services at a formal reception in the Blue Room in 1888. Young Mrs. Cleveland greets a lady escorted by Maj. Gen. John M. Schofield, USA, of Civil War renown.

DATE DUE

Fic
Mar
Martin, Ann M.

Jessi Ramsey, pet-
sitter

$10.50

Jessi Ramsey, Pet-sitter

THE BABY-SITTERS CLUB
titles in Large-Print Editions:

Jessi Ramsey, Pet-sitter
Ann M. Martin

Gareth Stevens Publishing
MILWAUKEE

For a free color catalog describing Gareth Stevens' list of high-quality books,
call 1-800-542-2595 (USA) or 1-800-461-9120 (Canada).
Gareth Stevens' Fax: (414) 225-0377.

Library of Congress Cataloging-in-Publication Data available upon request from publisher.
Fax: (414) 225-0377 for the attention of the Publishing Records Department.

ISBN 0-8368-1243-3

Published by Gareth Stevens, Inc., 1555 North RiverCenter Drive, Suite 201, Milwaukee,
Wisconsin 53212 in large print by arrangement with Scholastic Inc., 555 Broadway, New York,
New York 10012.

1 2 3 4 5 6 7 8 9 99 98 97 96 95 94

Printed in the United States of America

*This book is for my friends
Nicole, Anna, Rebecca,
Katie, and Alison*

CHAPTER 1

"**M**eow, meow, meow. Purr, purr."

I leaned over the edge of my bed and peered down at the floor.

"Pet me," said a small voice.

It wasn't a talking animal. It was my sister, Becca, pretending she was a cat.

I patted the top of her head but said, "Becca, I really have to do my homework."

"Then how come you're lying on your bed?" asked Becca, getting to her feet.

"Because this is a comfortable way to work."

"You're supposed to sit at your desk."

This is true. My parents believe that home-work magically gets done better if you're sitting up than if you're lying down.

I sighed. Then I changed the subject, which usually distracts Becca. "Why are you a cat tonight?" I asked her.

She shrugged. "I'm trying all the animals. It's fun to pretend."

The night before, Becca had been a dog, the night before that, a horse.

"Well, kitty, let me finish my work," I said.

"Meow," replied Becca, who dropped to her hands and knees and crawled into the hallway.

Becca is eight and has a big imagination. If she weren't so shy, she'd probably make a really terrific actress, but she has awful stage fright.

I do not have stage fright, which is lucky since I'm a ballet dancer and have to perform in front of audiences all the time.

I guess I should stop and introduce myself. I am Jessi Ramsey, and I'm eleven and in sixth grade. "Jessi" is short for "Jessica." (And "Becca" is short for "Rebecca," as if you couldn't have guessed.) Becca and I live with our parents and our baby brother, Squirt. Squirt's real name is John Philip Ramsey, Jr. When he was born, he was so tiny that the nurses in the hospital started calling him Squirt. Now his nickname seems sort of funny. Well, it always has been funny, but it seems especially funny since Squirt, who has just learned to walk, is now the size of most other babies his age.

Anyway, as I said before, I'm a ballet dancer. I've been taking dance classes for years. My ballet school is in Stamford, which isn't too far from Stoneybrook, Connecticut, where my

2

family and I live. We haven't lived here long, though. We moved to Connecticut from New Jersey just a few months ago when my dad was offered a job he couldn't turn down.

Oh, something else about my family — we're black. Actually, that's much more important than I'm making it sound. You know what? It wasn't so important when we were living in Oakley, New Jersey. Our old neighborhood was mixed black and white, and so was my ballet school and my regular school. But believe it or not, we are one of the few black families in all of Stoneybrook. In fact, I'm the only black student in my whole grade. When we first moved here, some people weren't very nice to us. Some were even mean. But things have settled down and are getting better. Becca and I are making friends. Actually, I have a lot more friends than Becca does. There are two reasons for this: one, I'm not shy; two, I belong to the Baby-sitters Club. (More about that later.)

My mother is wonderful and so is my father. We're a very close family. Mama, Daddy, Becca, Squirt, and me. No pets. We've never had a pet, although Becca apparently wishes we had one. (Sometimes I do, too, for that matter.)

In case you're wondering what the Baby-sitters Club is, let me tell you about it. It's very important to me because that's where I found most of my friends. The club is really a business, a sitting business. It was started by Kristy Thomas, who's the president. There are six of us in the club. We sit for kids in our neighborhoods, and we get lots of jobs and have lots of fun.

My best friend in Stoneybrook is Mallory Pike. Mal and I have a lot of classes together at Stoneybrook Middle School. And Mal is the one who got me into the Baby-sitters Club. The girls needed another member and ended up taking both of us. We were just getting to be friends then — and now that we've been in the club together for awhile, we're best friends. (I have another best friend in Oakley — my cousin Keisha.)

Anyway, the people in the club are Mallory, Kristy, me, plus Claudia Kishi, Mary Anne Spier, and Dawn Schafer. Two people who are sort of part of the club but who don't come to our meetings are our associate members, Logan Bruno and Shannon Kilbourne. (I'll tell you more about them later.) It's funny that us six club members work so well together, because boy, are we different. We have different personalities, different tastes, different looks, and different kinds of families.

4

Kristy Thomas, our president, is . . . well, talk about not shy. Kristy is direct and outgoing. Sometimes she can be loud and bossy. But basically she's really nice. And she's always full of ideas. Kristy is thirteen and in eighth grade. (So are all the club members, except Mal and me.) She has this long brown hair and is pretty, but doesn't pay much attention to her looks. I mean, she never bothers with makeup, and she always wears jeans, a turtleneck, a sweater, and sneakers. Kristy's family is sort of interesting. Her parents are divorced, and for the longest time, Kristy lived with just her mom, her two older brothers, Sam and Charlie (they're in high school), and her little brother, David Michael, who's seven now. But when her mom met this millionaire, Watson Brewer, and got remarried, things sure changed for Kristy. For one thing, Watson moved Kristy's family into his mansion, which is on the other side of Stoneybrook. Kristy used to live next door to Mary Anne Spier and across the street from Claudia Kishi. Now she's in a new neighborhood. For another thing, Kristy acquired a little stepsister and stepbrother — Watson's children from his first marriage. Karen is six and Andrew is four. Although it took Kristy some time to adjust to her new life, she sure loves Karen and Andrew. They're among her favorite baby-sitting charges. Kristy's family has two pets — an adorable puppy named Shannon and a fat old cat named Boo-Boo.

The vice-president of the Baby-sitters Club is Claudia Kishi, and she is totally cool. I think she's the coolest person I know. (I mean, except for movie stars or people like that.) Claud is just awesome-looking. She's Japanese-American and has gorgeous, *long*, jet-black hair; dark, almond-shaped eyes; and a clear complexion. Really. She could be on TV as the "after" part of a pimple medicine commercial. Claud loves art, Nancy Drew mysteries, and junk food, and she hates school. She's smart, but she's a terrible student. (Unfortunately, her older sister, Janine, is a genius, which makes Claudia's grades look even worse.) Claudia also loves fashion, and you should see her clothes. They are amazing, always wild. Like, she'll wear a miniskirt, black tights, push-down socks, high-top sneakers, a shirt she's painted or decorated herself, and big earrings she's made. Her hair might be pulled into a ponytail and held in place with not one but six or seven puffy ponytail holders, a row of them cascading down her hair. I'm always fascinated by Claudia. Claud lives with Janine, her parents, and her grandmother, Mimi. The Kishis don't have any pets.

Mary Anne Spier is the club secretary. She lives across the street from Claudia. And, until Kristy's family moved, she lived next door to the Thomases. Mary Anne and Kristy are best friends, and have been pretty much for life. (Dawn is Mary Anne's other best friend.) I've always thought this was interesting, since Mary Anne and Kristy are not alike at all. Mary Anne is shy and quiet and, well, sort of romantic. (She's the only club member who has a steady boyfriend. And guess who he is — Logan Bruno, one of our associate members!) Mary Anne is also a good listener and a patient person. Her mom died years ago, so Mary Anne's father raised her, and for the longest time, he was strict with her. Boy, was he strict. I didn't know Mary Anne then, but I've heard that Mr. Spier made all these rules, and there was practically nothing she was allowed to do. Lately, Mr. Spier has relaxed, though. He won't let Mary Anne get her ears pierced, but at least she can go out with Logan sometimes, and she can choose her own clothes. Since she's been allowed to do that, she's started dressing *much* better — not as wildly as Claudia, but she cares about how she looks, unlike Kristy. Mary Anne's family is just her and her dad and her gray kitten, Tigger.

Dawn Schafer is the treasurer of the Baby-sitters Club. I like Dawn. She's neat. Dawn is neither loud like Kristy nor shy like Mary Anne. She's an individual. She'd never go along with something just because other people were doing it. And she always sticks up for what she believes in. Dawn is basically a California girl. She moved to Connecticut about a year ago, but she still longs for warm weather and she loves health food. She even *looks* like a California girl with her white-blonde hair and her sparkling blue eyes. Although you'd never know it, Dawn has been through some tough times lately. When she moved here, she came with her mother and her younger brother, Jeff — her parents had just gotten divorced. Mrs. Schafer wanted to live in Stoneybrook because she'd grown up here, but that put three thousand miles between Dawn's mother and Dawn's father. As if the divorce and the move weren't enough, Jeff finally decided he couldn't handle the East Coast and moved back to California, so now Dawn's family is cracked in two, like a broken plate. But Dawn seems to be handling things okay. Luckily, she has her best friend (Mary Anne), and she and her mother are *extremely* close. Just so you know, the Schafers live in a neat old farmhouse that has a secret passage (honest), and they don't have any pets.

Then there's Mallory. Mallory Pike and I are the club's two junior officers. All that means is that we're too young to baby-sit at night unless we're sitting for our own brothers and sisters. Speaking of brothers and sisters, Mal has *seven* of them. She comes from the biggest family I know. Apart from that, and apart from the fact that Mal is white and I'm black, we're probably more alike than any two other club members. We both love to read books, especially horse stories, we both enjoy writing (but Mal enjoys it more than I do), we both wear glasses (mine are only for reading), and we both think our parents treat us kind of like babies. However, there was a recent breakthrough in which we convinced our parents to let us get our ears pierced! After that, Mal was even allowed to have her hair cut decently, but I'm still working on that angle. Neither of us is sure what we want to be when we grow the rest of the way up. I *might* want to be a professional dancer and Mal *might* want to be an author or an author/illustrator, but we figure we have time to decide these things. Right now, we're just happy being eleven-year-old baby-sitters.

Oh, one other similarity between Mal and me. Neither of us has a pet. I don't know if Mal wants one — she's never mentioned it —

but I bet her brothers and sisters do. Just like Becca.

"Hiss, hiss."

Becca was in my doorway. She was lying on her stomach.

"Now what are you?" I asked.

"I'll give you a hint." Becca flicked her tongue out of her mouth.

"Ew, ew!" I cried. "You're a snake. Slither away from me!"

Giggling, Becca did as she was told.

I went back to my homework, but I couldn't concentrate. Not because of Becca, but because of next week. I was going to have next week off. Well, sort of. Ordinarily, my afternoons are busy. When school is out, I go either to a ballet class or to my steady sitting job. My steady job is for Matt and Haley Braddock, two really great kids. But next week, my ballet school would be closed and the Braddocks were going on a vacation — even though school was in session. So, except for school and meetings of the Baby-sitters Club, I would be free, free, free! What would I do with all those spare hours? I wondered. Easy. I could put in extra practice time, I could read. The possibilities were endless!

CHAPTER 2

"Hi! Hi, you guys! Sorry I'm late." I rushed breathlessly into the Wednesday meeting of the Baby-sitters Club.

"You're not late," said Kristy, our president. "You're just the last one here."

"As always," I added.

"Well, don't worry about it. But it *is* five-thirty and time to begin." Kristy sounded very businesslike.

Mallory patted the floor next to her, so I shoved aside some of Claudia's art materials and sat down. We always sit on the floor. And Dawn, Mary Anne, and Claudia always sit on Claudia's bed. Guess where Kristy sits—in a director's chair, wearing a visor, as if she were the queen or something.

Club meetings are held in Claudia Kishi's room. This is because she's the only one of us who has a phone in her bedroom, and her own personal, private phone number, which makes it easy for our clients to reach us.

Hmmm. . . . I think I better stop right here, before I get ahead of myself. I'll tell you how the club got started and how it works; then the meeting won't sound so confusing.

The club began with Kristy, as I said before. She got the idea for it over a year ago. That was when she and her mom and brothers were still living across the street from Claudia, and her mother was just starting to date Watson Brewer. Usually, when Mrs. Thomas wasn't going to be around, Kristy or Sam or Charlie would take care of David Michael. But one day when Mrs. Thomas announced that she was going to need a sitter, neither Kristy nor one of her older brothers was free. So Mrs. Thomas got on the phone and began calling around for another sitter. Kristy watched her mom make one call after another. And as she watched, that mind of hers was clicking away, thinking that Mrs. Thomas sure could save time if she could make one call and reach several sitters at once. And that was when Kristy got the idea for the Baby-sitters Club!

She talked to Mary Anne and Claudia, Claudia talked to Stacey McGill, a new friend of hers, and the four of them formed the club. (I'll tell you more about Stacey in a minute.)

The girls decided that they'd meet three times a week in Claudia's room (because of the phone). They'd advertise their club in the local paper and around the neighborhood, saying that four reliable sitters could be reached every Monday, Wednesday, and Friday afternoon from five-thirty until six.

Well, Kristy's great idea worked! Right away, the girls started getting jobs. People really liked them. In fact, the club was so successful that when Dawn moved to Stoneybrook and wanted to join, the girls needed her. And later, when Stacey McGill had to move back to New York City, they needed to replace her. (Stacey's move, by the way, was unfortunate, because in the short time the McGills lived in Stoney-brook, she and Claudia became best friends. Now they really miss each other.) Anyway, Mal and I joined the club to help fill the hole left by Stacey, and Shannon Kilbourne and Logan Bruno were made associate members. That means that they don't come to meetings, but if a job is offered that the rest of us can't take, we call one of them to see if they're interested. They're our backups. Believe it or not, we do have to call them every now and then.

Each person in the club holds a special

position or office. There are the associate members, Shannon and Logan, and there are the junior officers, Mal and me. The other positions are more important. (I'm not putting the rest of us down or anything. This is just the truth.)

As president, Kristy is responsible for running the meetings, getting good ideas, and, well, just being in charge, I guess. Considering that president is the most important office of all, Kristy doesn't do a lot of work. I mean, not compared to what the other girls do. But then, the club *was* her idea, so I think she deserves to be its president.

Claudia Kishi, our vice-president, doesn't really have a lot to do, either, but the rest of us invade her room three times a week and tie up her phone line. Plus, a lot of our clients forget when our meetings are held and call at other times with sitting jobs. Claud has to handle those calls. I think she deserves to be vice-president.

As secretary, Mary Anne Spier is probably the hardest-working officer. She's in charge of the record book, which is where we keep track of all club information: our clients' addresses and phone numbers, the money in the treasury (well, that's really Dawn's department), and most importantly, the appointment calendar.

14

Poor Mary Anne has to keep track of everybody's schedules (my ballet lessons, Claud's art classes, dentist appointments, etc.) *and* all of our baby-sitting jobs. When a call comes in, it's up to Mary Anne to see who's free. Mary Anne is neat and careful and hasn't made a scheduling mistake yet.

This is a miracle.

Dawn, our treasurer, is responsible for collecting dues from us club members every Monday, and for keeping enough money in the treasury so that we can pay Charlie, Kristy's oldest brother, to drive her to and from meetings, since she lives so far away now. The money is spent on other things, too, but we make sure we always have enough for Charlie. What else is the money spent on? Well, fun things, like food for club slumber parties. Also new materials for Kid-Kits.

I guess I haven't told you about Kid-Kits yet. They were one of Kristy's ideas. A Kid-Kit is a box (we each have one) that's been decorated and filled with our old toys and books and games, as well as a few new items such as crayons or sticker books. We bring them with us on some of our jobs and kids love them. The kits make us very popular baby-sitters! Anyway, every now and then we

15

need treasury money to buy new crayons or something for the kits.

The last thing you need to know about is our club notebook. The notebook is like a diary. In it, each of us sitters has to write up every single job she goes on. Then we're supposed to read it once a week to find out what's been going on. Even though most of us don't like writing in the notebook, I have to admit that it's helpful. When I read it, I find out what's happening with the kids our club sits for, and also about baby-sitting problems and how they were handled. (The club notebook was Kristy's idea, of course.)

"Order, order!" Kristy was saying.

I had just settled myself on the floor.

"Wait a sec," Claudia interrupted. "Doesn't anyone want something to eat?"

Remember I said Claudia likes junk food? Well, that may have been an understatement. Claud *loves* junk food. She loves it so much that her parents have told her to stop eating so much of it. But Claud can't. She buys it anyway and then hides it in her room. At the moment, she's got a bag of potato chips under her bed, a package of licorice sticks in a drawer of her jewelry box, and a bag of M&M's in the pencil case in her notebook. She's very generous with it. She offers it around at the

16

beginning of each meeting since we're starved by this time of day. And we eat up. (Well, sometimes Dawn doesn't since she's so into health food, but she *will* eat crackers or pretzels.)

"Ahem," said Kristy.

"Oh, come on. You know you'll eat something if I get it out," Claudia told her. Claudia usually stands up to Kristy.

"All right." Kristy sounded as cross as a bear, but this didn't prevent her from eating a handful of M&M's.

When the candy had been passed around, Kristy said, "*Now* are we ready?"

(She sure can be bossy.)

"Ready, Ms. Thomas," Claudia replied in a high, squeaky voice.

Everyone laughed, even Kristy.

We talked about some club business, and then the phone began to ring. The first call was from Mrs. Newton. She's the mother of Jamie and Lucy, two of the club's favorite sitting charges. Mary Anne scheduled Dawn for the job. Then the phone rang twice more. Jobs for Mal and Mary Anne. I was sort of relieved that so far, none of the jobs had been for next week. I was still looking forward to my week off.

Ring, ring.

Another call.

Claudia answered the phone. She listened for a moment and then began to look confused. "Mrs. Mancusi?" she said.

Kristy glanced up from the notebook, which she'd been reading. "Mrs. Mancusi?" she whispered to the rest of us. "She doesn't have any kids."

We listened to Claud's end of the conversation, but all she would say were things like, "Mm-hmm," and "Oh, I see," and "Yes, that's too bad." Then, after a long pause, she said, "Well, this is sort of unusual, but let me talk to the other girls and see what they say. Someone will call you back in about five minutes. . . . Yes. . . . Okay. . . . Okay, 'bye."

Claudia hung up the phone and looked up from some notes she'd been making. She found the rest of us staring at her.

"Well?" said Kristy.

"Well, the Mancusis need a pet-sitter," Claudia began.

"A *pet*-sitter?" Kristy practically jumped down Claud's throat.

"Yeah, let me explain," Claud rushed on. "They're going on vacation next week. They've had this really nice vacation planned for months now. And you know all those animals they have?"

"Their house is a zoo," Mary Anne spoke up.

"I know," Claud replied. "All I could hear in the background was barking and squawking and chirping."

"What's the point?" asked Kristy rudely.

"Sheesh," said Claud. "Give me a minute. The *point* is that the Mancusis had a pet-sitter all lined up and he just called and canceled."

"That is *so* irresponsible," commented Mallory.

"I know," agreed Claud. "Now the Mancusis can't take their vacation, not unless they find a pet-sitter."

"Oh, but Claudia," wailed Kristy, "how could you even *think* about another pet-sitting job?"

"Another one?" I asked.

"Yeah," said Kristy. "The very first job I got when we started the club — my first job offer at our first official meeting — was for two Saint Bernard dogs, and it was a disaster."

I couldn't help giggling. "It was?" I said. "What happened?"

"Oh, you name it. The dogs, Pinky and Buffy, were sweet, but they were big and gallumphing and they liked making mischief. What an afternoon that was! Anyway, I swore we would never pet-sit again."

19

"But Kristy," protested Claudia, "if the Mancusis can't find a pet-sitter, they'll have to cancel their dream vacation."

Kristy sighed. "All right. Suppose one of us was crazy enough to *want* to pet-sit — don't the Mancusis need someone every day?"

"Yes, for a few hours every day next week, plus the weekend before and the weekend after. They're leaving this Saturday and returning Sunday, a week later."

"Well, that kills it," said Kristy. "I don't want any of my sitters tied up for a week."

At that, I heard Dawn mutter something that sounded like . . . well, it didn't sound nice. And I saw her poke Mary Anne, who mouthed "bossy" to her. Then Mal whispered to me, "Who does Kristy think she is? The queen?"

All of which gave me the courage to say (nervously), "Um, you know how the Braddocks are going away?"

"Yes?" replied the other club members, turning toward me.

"Well . . . well, um, my ballet school is closed next week, too. Remember? So I'm available. For the whole week. I could take care of the Mancusis' pets. I mean, if they want me to." (So much for my week of freedom.)

"Perfect!" exclaimed Claud. "I'll call them right now."

"Not so fast!" interrupted Kristy. "I haven't given my permission yet."

"Your per*mis*sion?" cried the rest of us.

Kristy must have realized she'd gone too far then. Her face turned bright red.

"Listen, just because *you* had a bad pet-sitting experience — " Dawn began.

"I know, I know. I'm sorry." Kristy turned toward me. "Go ahead," she said. "You may take the job."

"Thank you."

Claud called Mrs. Mancusi back, as promised. As you can probably imagine, Mrs. Mancusi was delighted to have a sitter. She asked to speak to me. After thanking me several times, she said, "When could you come by? My husband and I will have to show you how to care for the animals. There are quite a lot of them, you know."

After some discussion, we decided on Friday evening, right after supper. It was the only time the Mancusis and I were all free. Since the Mancusis live near my house, I knew that would be okay with my parents.

I hung up the phone. "Gosh, the Mancusis sure are going to pay me well."

"They better," Kristy replied. "I don't think Claud told you exactly how many pets they have. There are three dogs, five cats, some birds and hamsters, two guinea pigs, a snake, lots of fish, and a bunch of rabbits and turtles."

I gulped. What had I gotten myself into?

CHAPTER 3

As soon as I saw Mr. and Mrs. Mancusi, I realized I knew them — and they knew me. They're always out walking their dogs, and I'm often out walking Squirt in his stroller, or baby-sitting for some little kids. The Mancusis and I wave and smile at each other. Until I met them, I just didn't know their names, or that beside their dogs they owned a small zoo.

This is what I heard when I rang their doorbell: *Yip-yip, meow, mew, chirp, cheep, squawk, squeak, woof-woof-woof.*

By the way, I am a pretty good speller and every now and then my teacher gives me a list of really hard words to learn to spell and use in sentences. On the last list was the word *cacophony*. It means a jolting, nonharmonious mixture of sounds. Well, those animal voices at the Mancusis' were not jolting, but they sure were nonharmonious and they sure were a mixture.

The door opened. There was Mrs. Mancusi's pleasant face. "Oh! It's *you!*" she exclaimed, just as I said, "Oh! The dogwalker!"

"Come on in." Smiling, Mrs. Mancusi held the door open for me.

I stepped inside and the cacophony grew louder.

"SHH! SHH!" said Mrs. Mancusi urgently. "Sit. . . . Sit, Cheryl."

A Great Dane sat down obediently. Soon the barking stopped. Then the birds quieted down.

Mrs. Mancusi smiled at me. "So you're Jessi," she said. "I've seen you around a lot lately."

"We moved here a few months ago," I told her, not mentioning that, in general, the neighbors hadn't been too . . . talkative.

Mrs. Mancusi nodded. "Is that your brother I see you with sometimes?" she asked. (A bird swooped into the room and landed on her shoulder while a white kitten tottered to her ankles and began twining himself around them.)

"Yes," I answered. "That's Squirt. Well, his real name is John Philip Ramsey, Junior. I have a sister, too. Becca. She's eight. But," I added, "we don't have any pets."

Mrs. Mancusi looked fondly at her animals. "I guess that makes us even," she said. "My

24

husband and I don't have any children, but we have plenty of pets. Well, I should start — "

At that moment, Mr. Mancusi strode into the front hall. After more introductions, his wife said, "I was just about to have Jessi meet the animals."

Mr. Mancusi nodded. "Let's start with the dogs. I guess you've already seen Cheryl," he said, patting the Great Dane.

"Right," I replied. I pulled a pad of paper and a pencil out of my purse so I could take notes.

But Mr. Mancusi stopped me. "Don't bother," he said. "Everything is written down. We'll show you where in a minute. Just give the animals a chance to get to know you. In fact," he went on, "why don't you talk to each one? That would help them to feel more secure with you."

"Talk to them?" I repeated.

"Sure. Say anything you want. Let them hear the sound of your voice."

I felt like a real jerk, but I patted the top of Cheryl's head (which is softer than it looks) and said, "Hi, Cheryl. I'm Jessi. I'm going to walk you and take care of you next week."

Cheryl look at me with her huge eyes — and yawned.

We all laughed. "I guess I'm not very impressive," I said.

On the floor in the living room lay an apricot-colored poodle.

"That's Pooh Bear," said Mrs. Mancusi. "Believe it or not, she's harder to walk than Cheryl. Cheryl is big but obedient. Pooh Bear is small but devilish."

I knelt down and patted Pooh Bear's curly fur. "Nice girl," I said. (Pooh Bear stared at me.) "Nice girl . . . Um, I'm Jessi. We're going to take walks next week." Then I added in a whisper, "I hope you'll behave."

The Mancusis' third dog is a golden retriever named Jacques. Jacques was napping in the kitchen. He tiredly stuck his paw in my lap when I sat down next to him, but he barely opened his eyes.

"Now Jacques," began Mr. Mancusi, "is only a year old. Still pretty much a puppy. He tries hard to behave, but if Pooh Bear acts up, he can't help following her lead."

"Right," I said. I tried to think of something creative to say to Jacques, but finally just told him I was looking forward to walking him.

"All right. Cats next," said Mrs. Mancusi, picking up the kitten. "This little fluffball is Powder. He's just two and a half months old. But don't worry. He knows how to take care of himself. Also, his mother is here."

"Hi, Powder," I said, putting my face up to his soft fur.

Then Mrs. Mancusi set Powder on the ground and we went on a cat-hunt, in search of the other four. Here's who we found: Crosby, an orange tiger cat who can fetch like a dog; Ling-Ling, a Siamese cat with a *very* loud voice; Tom, a patchy gray cat with a wicked temper; and Rosie, Powder's mother.

Next we went into the Mancusis' den, where there were several large bird cages holding parakeets, cockatoos, and macaws.

"Awk?" said one bird as we entered the room. "Where's the beef? Where's the beef? Where's the beef?"

Mr. Mancusi laughed. "That's Frank," he said. "He used to watch a lot of TV. I mean, before we got him." I must have looked astonished, because he went on, "It's natural for some birds to imitate what they hear. Frank can say other things, too, can't you, Frank?"

Frank blinked his eyes but remained silent.

"See, he isn't really trained," added Mr. Mancusi. "He only talks when he feels like it."

Mrs. Mancusi removed the bird that had landed on her shoulder earlier and placed him in one of the cages. "Often, we leave the cages open," she told me, "and let the birds fly around the house. I'd suggest it for next week, but most people don't feel comfortable trying to get the birds back in the cages, so maybe that's not such a good idea."

It certainly didn't sound like a good one to me.

I started to leave the den, but Mr. Mancusi was looking at me, so I peered into the bird cages and spoke to Frank and his friends.

In the kitchen were a cage full of hamsters and a much bigger cage, almost a pen, that contained two guinea pigs. I looked in at the hamsters first.

"They're nocturnal," said Mrs. Mancusi. "They're up all night and asleep all day. You should see them in the daytime. They sleep in a big pile in the middle of the cage."

I smiled. Then I looked at the guinea pigs. They were pretty interesting, too. They were big, bigger than the hamsters, and they were sniffing around their cage. Every so often one of them would let out a whistle.

"The guinea pigs are Lucy and Ricky. You know, from the *I Love Lucy* show," said Mr. Mancusi. "They shouldn't be any trouble, and they *love* to be taken out of their cage for exercise."

"Okay," I said, thinking that Lucy and Ricky looked like fun.

28

We left the kitchen and walked toward a sun porch. The job, I decided, was going to be big but manageable. I could handle it.

Then I met the reptiles.

The aquarium full of turtles wasn't *too* bad. I don't love turtles, but I don't mind them.

What was bad was Barney.

Barney is a snake. He's very small and he isn't poisonous, but he's still a snake. A wriggling, scaly, tongue-flicking snake.

Thank goodness the Mancusis didn't ask me to touch Barney or take him out of his cage. All they said was I'd have to feed him. Well, I could do that. Even if I did have to feed him the insects and earthworms that the Mancusis had a supply of. I'd just try to wear oven mitts. Or maybe I could stand ten feet away from his cage and throw the worms in.

"Nice Barney. Good Barney," I whispered when the Mancusis stopped and waited for me to talk to him. "You don't hurt me — and I'll stay away from you."

Next the Mancusis showed me their fish (about a million of them), and their rabbits (Fluffer-Nut, Cindy, Toto, and Robert). And after *that*, they took me back to the kitchen, where they had posted lists of instructions for caring for each type of animal, plus everything I'd need to feed and exercise them — food dishes, chow (several kinds), leashes, etc. I would be going to their house twice a day. Early in the morning to walk the dogs and feed the dogs and cats, and after school to walk the dogs again and to feed all the animals.

When I said good-night to the Mancusis I felt slightly overwhelmed but confident. The job was a big one, but I'd met the animals, and I'd seen the lists of instructions. They were very clear. If the animals would just behave, everything would be fine . . . probably.

Saturday was my test. The Mancusis left late in the morning. By the middle of the afternoon, Cheryl, Pooh Bear, and Jacques would be ready for a walk. After that, the entire zoo would need feeding. So at three o'clock I headed for the Mancusis' with the key to their front door. I let myself in (the cacophony began immediately), managed to put leashes on the dogs, and took them for a nice, long walk. The walk went fine except for when Pooh Bear spotted a squirrel. For just a moment, the dogs were taking *me* on a walk instead of the other way around. But the squirrel disappeared, the dogs calmed down, and we returned to the Mancusis' safely.

When the dog's leashes had been hung up, I played with the cats and the guinea pigs. I let the rabbits out for awhile. Then it was feeding time. Dog chow in the dog dishes, cat chow in the cat dishes, fish food in the tank, rabbit food in the hutch, guinea pig food in the guinea pig cage, bird food in the bird cages, turtle food in the aquarium, hamster food in the hamster cage, and finally it was time for . . . Barney.

I looked in his cage. There he was, sort of twined around a rock. He wasn't moving, but his eyes were open. I think he was looking at me. I found a spatula in the kitchen, used it to slide the lid of Barney's cage back, and then, quick as a wink, I dropped his food inside and shoved the lid closed.

Barney never moved.

Well, that was easy, I thought as I made a final check on all the animals. A lot of them were eating. But the hamsters were sound asleep. They were all sleeping in a pile, just like Mrs. Mancusi had said they would do, except for one very fat hamster. He lay curled in a corner by himself. What was wrong? Was he some sort of outcast? I decided not to worry, since the Mancusis hadn't said anything about him.

I found my house key and got ready to go. My first afternoon as a pet-sitter had been a success, I decided.

CHAPTER 4

Sundae

Oh, my lord waht a day. I babbysat for Jamie newton and he invinted Nina marshal over to play. That was fine but I thoght it would be fun for the kids to see all the amials over at the ~~Me War~~ makusees or however you spell it. So I took them over but Jamie was afriad of the ginny pigs so we took the kids and the dogs on a walk but we ran into Chewey and you now waht that means -- trouble.

Well, it was trouble, as Claudia said, but it wasn't too bad. I mean, I'm sure we've all been in worse trouble.

Anyway, on Sunday afternoon when I was about to head back to the Mancusis', Claudia was baby-sitting for Jamie Newton. Jamie is four, and one of the club's favorite clients. Kristy, Mary Anne, and Claudia were sitting for him long before there even *was* a Baby-sitters Club. Now Jamie has an eight-month-old sister, Lucy, but Claud was only in charge of Jamie that day. His parents were going visiting, and they were taking Lucy with them.

When Claudia arrived at the Newtons', she found an overexcited Jamie. He was bouncing around, singing songs, making noises, and annoying everybody — which is not like Jamie.

"I don't know where he got all this energy," said Mrs. Newton tiredly. "I hope you don't mind, but I told him he could invite Nina Marshall to play. Maybe they'll run off some of Jamie's energy. Anyway, Nina is on her way over."

"Oh, that's fine," said Claud, who has sat for Nina and her little sister Eleanor many times.

The Newtons left then, and Claudia took Jamie outside to wait for Nina.

"Miss Mary Mack, Mack, Mack," sang Jamie, jumping along the front walk in time to his song, "all dressed in black, black, black, with silver buttons, buttons, buttons, all down her back, back, back. She jumped so high, high, high," (Jamie's jumping became even bouncier at that part) "she touched the sky, sky, sky, and didn't come back, back, back, till the Fourth of July, ly, ly!"

Lord, thought Claudia, I have hardly ever seen Jamie so wound up.

Unfortunately, Jamie didn't calm down much when Nina arrived. Claudia suggested a game of catch — and in record time, an argument broke out.

"If you miss the ball, you have to give up your turn," announced Jamie.

"Do not!" cried Nina indignantly.

"Do too!"

"Do not!"

"Whoa!" said Claudia, taking the ball from Jamie. "I think that's enough catch. Let's find something else to do today."

"Miss Mary Mack, Mack, Mack — " began Jamie.

Claudia didn't want to listen to the song

again. She racked her brain for some kind of diversion — and had an idea. "Hey, you guys," she said excitedly, "how would you like to go to a place where you can see lots of animals?"

"The *zoo?*" exclaimed Nina.

"Almost," Claud replied. "*Do* you want to see some animals?"

"Yes!" cried Jamie and Nina.

"Okay," said Claud. "Nina, I'm just going to call your parents and tell them where we're going. Then we can be on our way."

Fifteen minutes later the Mancusis' doorbell was ringing. I had arrived to do the afternoon feeding and walking. As you can imagine, I was surprised. Who would be ringing their bell? Somebody who didn't know they were on vacation, I decided.

I peeked out the front windows before I went ahead and opened the door. And standing on the stoop were Claud, Jamie Newton, and Nina Marshall! I let them in right away.

"Hi, you guys!" I exclaimed.

"Hi," replied Claud. "I hope we're not bothering you."

"Nope. I just got here. I'm getting ready to walk the dogs."

"Oh," said Claudia. "Well, if it isn't too much trouble, could Jamie and Nina look at the animals? We're sort of on a field trip."

I giggled. "Sure. I'll show you around."

But I didn't have to do much showing at first. Pooh Bear was lolling on the floor in the front hall, and then Rosie wandered in, followed by Powder, who was batting his mother's tail.

Jamie and Nina began patting Pooh Bear and Rosie and trying to cuddle Powder. When the animals' patience wore out, I took Jamie and Nina by the hand and walked them to the bird cages. Frank very obligingly called out, "Where's the beef? Where's the beef?" and then, "Two, two, two mints in one!"

"Gosh," said Jamie, "I know a song you'd like, Frank." He sang Miss Mary Mack to him. "See?" he went on. "Miss Mary Mack, Mack, Mack. It's kind of like 'Two, two, two mints in one!'"

Next I showed the kids the rabbits and then the guinea pigs.

"We can take the guinea pigs out — " I started to say.

But Jamie let loose a shriek. "NO! NO! Don't take them out!"

"Hey," said Claud, wrapping Jamie in her arms, "don't worry. We won't take them out. What's wrong?"

"They're beasties!" Jamie cried. "They come from outer space. I saw them on TV."

"Oh Jamie," Claud said gently. "They aren't beasties. There's no such — "

"*Beast*ies?" exclaimed Nina.

"Yes," said Jamie. "They're mean and awful. They bite people and then they take over the world."

"WAHHH!" wailed Nina. "I want to go home!"

I nudged Claudia. "Listen," I said, "I have to walk the dogs now anyway. Why don't you and Jamie and Nina come with me?"

"Good idea," agreed Claudia.

Jamie and Nina calmed down as they watched me put the leashes on Pooh Bear, Jacques, and Cheryl.

"Can Nina and I walk a dog?" asked Jamie.

"I'd really like to let you," I told him, "But the dogs are my responsibility. The Mancusis think *I'm* caring for them, so I better walk them. I'll bet you've never seen one person walk three dogs at the same time."

"No," agreed Jamie, as I locked the front door behind us. He and Nina watched, wide-eyed, as I took the leashes in my right hand and the dogs practically pulled me to the sidewalk.

Claud laughed, I laughed, and Jamie and Nina shrieked with delight.

The beasties were forgotten.

"I'll walk you back to your neighborhood," I told Claudia.

"You mean *Cheryl* will walk us back to our neighborhood," said Claud with a grin.

Cheryl was trying hard to be obedient, but she's so big that even when she walked, Jamie and Nina had to run to keep up with her.

"Actually," I told Claudia, "Pooh Bear is the problem. She's the feisty one. And when she gets feisty, Jacques gets feisty."

"Well, so far so good," Claud replied.

And everything was still okay by the time we reached Claudia's house. Just a few more houses and Jamie would be home again.

That was when Chewbacca showed up.

Who is Chewbacca? He's the Perkinses' black Labrador retriever. The Perkinses are the family who moved into Kristy Thomas' old house, across the street from Claudia. We sit for them a lot, since they have three kids — Myriah, Gabbie, and Laura. But guess what? It's harder to take care of Chewy by himself than to take care of all three girls together. Chewy isn't mean; don't get me wrong. He's just mischievous. Like Cheryl, he's big and lovable, but he gets into things. You can almost hear him thinking, Let's see. *Now* what can I do? Chewy finds things, hides things, chases things. And when you walk him, you never know what might catch his eye — a falling leaf, a butterfly — and cause him to go on a doggie rampage.

"Uh-oh, Chewy's loose!" said Claudia.

"Go home, Chewy! Go on home!" I coaxed him. I pointed to the Perkinses' house (as if Chewy would know what that meant).

Jamie added, "Shoo! Shoo!"

Chewy grinned at us and then pranced right up to the Mancusis' dogs. He just made himself part of the bunch, even though he wasn't on a leash.

"Well, now what?" I said as we walked along. Cheryl and Jacques and Pooh Bear didn't seem the least bit upset — but what would I do with Chewy when we got back to the Mancusis'? . . . And what would happen if Chewy saw something that set him off?

"Turn around," suggested Claudia. "Let's walk Chewy back to his house."

Jamie, Nina, Claudia, Pooh Bear, Jacques, Cheryl, and I turned around and headed for the Perkinses'. But Chewy didn't come with us. He sat on the sidewalk and waited for us to come back to him.

"He is just too smart," remarked Jamie.

I rang the Perkinses' bell, hoping someone would go get Chewy, but nobody answered.

"I guess he'll just have to walk with us," I finally said.

We rejoined Chewy and set off. Chewy bunched up with the dogs again as if he'd been walking with them all his life.

"Oh, no! There's a squirrel!" Claudia cried softly. "Now what?"

Chewy looked at the squirrel. The squirrel looked at Chewy.

Pooh Bear looked at the squirrel. The squirrel looked at Pooh Bear. Then it ran up a tree.

Nothing.

The rest of the walk was like that. A leaf drifted to the ground in front of the dogs. "Uh-oh," said Nina. But nothing happened. A chipmunk darted across the sidewalk. We all held our breaths, sure that Chewy or Pooh Bear or maybe Jacques was going to go off his (or her) rocker. But the dogs were incredibly well-behaved. It was as if they were trying to drive us crazy with their good behavior.

We circled around Claudia's neighborhood and finally reached the Perkinses' again. This time they were home and glad to see Chewy. We left him there, and then Claud took Jamie and Nina home, and I returned to the Mancusis' with the dogs. I played with the cats and guinea pigs and rabbits, and I fed the animals. In the hamster cage, the fat one was still curled in a separate corner. I wondered if I should be worried about him. When I stroked him with my finger, he didn't even wake up. I decided to keep my eye on him.

CHAPTER 5

On Monday afternoon I raced to the Mancusis', gave the dogs a whirlwind walk, played with the animals, fed them, and then raced to Claudia's for a club meeting. I just made it.

When I reached Claudia's room, Kristy was already in the director's chair, visor in place, the club notebook in her lap. But it was only 5:28. Two more minutes until the meeting would officially begin. Dawn hadn't arrived yet. (For once I wasn't the last to arrive!) Claudia was frantically trying to read the last two pages of *The Clue of the Velvet Mask*, a Nancy Drew mystery. Mary Anne was examining her hair for split ends, and Mallory was blowing a gigantic bubble with strawberry gum.

I joined Mal on the floor.

"Hi," I said.

Mal just waved, since she was concentrating on her bubble.

"Hi, Jessi," said Claudia and Mary Anne.

But Kristy was engrossed in the notebook and didn't say anything. When Dawn came in, she snapped to attention, though.

"Order, please!" she called. "Come to order."

Reluctantly, Claudia put her book down. "Just one *paragraph* to go," she said.

"Well, nothing ever happens in the last paragraph," remarked Mary Anne. "The author just tells you which mystery Nancy's going to solve next."

"That's true."

"ORDER!" shouted Kristy.

Boy, was I glad I was already *in* order.

"Sheesh," said Claud.

Kristy ignored her. "Ahem," she said. "Dawn, how's the treasury?"

"It'll be great after I collect dues," replied Dawn.

Groan, groan, groan. Every Monday Dawn collects dues, and every Monday we groan about having to give her money. It's not as if it's any big surprise. But the same thing —

"Please pay attention!" barked Kristy.

My head snapped up. What was this? School?

I glanced at Mallory who mouthed, "Boss-lady" to me and nodded toward Kristy. Then I had to try not to laugh.

"All right," Kristy went on, "has everyone been reading the notebook?"

"Yes," we chorused. We *always* keep up with it.

"Okay," said Kristy. "If you're really reading it — "

"We are!" Claud exploded. "Sheesh, Kristy, what's with you lately? You're bossier than ever."

For a moment, Kristy softened. "Sorry," she said. "It's just that Charlie suddenly thinks he's the big shot of the world. Next year he'll be in college, you know. So he bosses Sam and David Michael and me around nonstop." Kristy paused. Then her face hardened into her "I am the president" look.

"But," she went on, "I *am* the president, which gives me the right to boss you club members around."

"Excuse me," said Claudia in an odd voice, and I wondered what was coming, "but as president just what else *do* you do — besides get ideas, which any of us could do."

"Oh, yeah?" said Kristy.

"Yeah."

"Well, what brilliant ideas have you had?"

"I believe," Mary Anne spoke up, "that Claudia was the one who designed the alphabet blocks that say The Baby-sitters Club. That's

44

our logo and we use it on every flier we give out."

"Thank you, Mary Anne," said Claudia. "And I believe that Mary Anne figured out who sent her the bad-luck charm, which was the first step in solving that mystery a while ago."

"And Mallory — " I began.

"Okay, okay, okay," said Kristy.

But the other girls weren't finished.

"I," said Dawn, "would like to know, Kristy, just what it is — "

Ring, ring.

We were so engrossed in what Dawn was saying that we didn't all dive for the phone as usual.

Ring, ring.

Finally Mary Anne answered it. She arranged a job for Mallory. Then the phone rang two more times. When *those* jobs had been set up, we looked expectantly at Dawn. (Well, Kristy didn't. She was glaring at us — all of us.)

Dawn picked up right where she'd left off. " — just what it is you do besides boss us around and get great ideas."

"I run the meetings."

"Big deal," said Claudia.

"Well, what do *you* do, Ms. Vice-President?" asked Kristy hotly.

"Besides donating my room and my phone to you three times a week," Claudia replied, "I have to take all those calls that come in when we're not meeting. And there are quite a few of them. You know that."

"And," spoke up Dawn, "*I* have to keep track of the money, collect dues every week — which isn't always easy — and be in charge of remembering to pay your brother, and of buying things for the Kid-Kits."

"*I*," said Mary Anne, "probably have the most complicated job of anybody." (No one disagreed with her.) "I have to schedule *every single* job any of us goes on. I have to keep track of our schedules, of our clients, their addresses, and how many kids are in their families. It is a huge job."

"And we do these jobs *in addition* to getting ideas," pointed out Dawn.

There was a moment of silence. Then Mary Anne said, "Okay. We have a problem. But I've got an idea. I suggest — "

"We do *not* have a problem," Kristy interrupted her. "Trust me, we don't. All you guys need to do is calm down and you'll see that things are actually in control." Kristy paused. When none of us said anything, she went on, "Okay, now I have a really important idea.

Forget this other stuff. To make sure that each of you is reading the notebook once a week, I'm going to draw up a checklist. Every Monday, in order to show me you've been keeping up with the notebook, you'll initial a box on the chart."

"*What?!*" exclaimed Claudia.

Dawn and Mary Anne gasped.

Mallory and I glanced at each other. We hadn't been saying much. We didn't want to get involved in a club fight. Since we're the newest and youngest members, we try to stay out of arguments. It's hard to know whose side to be on. We don't want to step on any toes. And the easiest way to do that is to keep our mouths shut.

But the other girls *wanted* us to take sides.

"Jessi, what do you think?" asked Claudia. "Mallory?"

I hesitated. "About the chart?" I finally said.

"Yes, about the chart."

"Well, um, I — I mean . . ." I looked at Mal.

"See," Mal began, "um, it — I . . ."

Claudia was thoroughly annoyed. "Forget it," she snapped.

"Kristy, there is absolutely no reason to make a checklist for us," said Dawn. "There's not even any reason to *ask* us if we've been reading the notebook. We always keep up with it. Each one of us. Don't we say yes every time you ask us about it?"

The argument was interrupted by several more job calls. But as soon as Mary Anne had made the arrangements, the club members went right back to their discussion.

"There's no need for the checklist," Dawn said again.

"Don't you trust us?" Mary Anne wanted to know.

Kristy sighed. "Of course I trust you. The checklist will just, well, prove to me that I can trust you. Plus, I won't have to ask you about reading the notebook anymore."

"But can't you *just trust* us?" said Mary Anne.

Kristy opened her mouth to answer the question, but Dawn spoke up instead.

"You know," she said, changing the subject, "personally, I am tired of having to collect dues on Mondays. Everyone groans and complains and makes me feel about *this* big." Dawn held her fingers a couple of inches apart.

"We don't mean to complain — " I started to tell Dawn.

But Claudia cut in with, "Well, *I'm* pretty tired of getting those job calls all the time. You know, some people don't even try to remember

48

when our meetings are. Mrs. Barrett hardly ever calls during meetings. She calls at nine o'clock on a Sunday night, or on a Tuesday afternoon, or — worst of all — at eight-thirty on a Saturday morning."

"And I," said Mary Anne, "am especially tired of scheduling. I'm tired of keeping track of dentist appointments and ballet lessons — "

"Sorry," I apologized again. (I am really wonderful at apologizing.)

"Oh, it's not your fault, Jessi. Everyone has things that need scheduling. In fact, that's the problem. I'm up to my ears in lessons and classes and dental visits. I've been doing this job for over a year now, and I'm just tired of it. That's all there is to it."

"What are you guys saying?" Kristy asked her friends.

"That I don't like scheduling," Mary Anne replied.

"And I don't like collecting dues," said Dawn.

"And I don't like all the phone calls," added Claudia.

I looked at Mal. Why didn't Kristy speak up? What did she not like about being president? Finally it occurred to me — nothing. There was nothing she didn't like because . . . because her job was pretty easy and fun. Conducting meetings, being in charge, getting ideas. Kristy sure had the easy job. (Mal and I did, too, but we had been *made* junior officers with hardly any club responsibilities. We hadn't had a say in the matter.)

I think we were all relieved when the meeting broke up. Well, I know Mal and I were, but it was hard to tell about the others. They left the meeting absolutely silently. Not a word was spoken.

Mal and I stood around on the sidewalk in front of the Kishis' until the other girls left. As soon as Mary Anne had disappeared into her house across the street, I said, "Whoa. Some meeting. What do you think, Mal?"

"I think," she replied, "that this is not a good sign. I also think that you and I might be asked to take sides soon."

"Probably," I agreed, "but it's going to be very important that we stay neutral. No taking sides at all."

CHAPTER 6

Tuesday

Oh, wow. I don't have words to describe what happened today. I could write down awful, disgusting, gross, shivery, blechh, but even those words don't say it all. I better just explain what happened. See, I was baby-sitting for Myriah and Gabbie Perkins, and I decided to take them over to the Mancusis' to visit the animals. I knew Claudia had done that with Jamie and Nina, and I thought it was a good idea. (How did I know Claudia had done that? Because I read the notebook, Kristy, that's how.) So I walked the girls over to the Mancusis'....

51

Mary Anne just loves sitting for the Perkinses. Remember them? They're the owners of Chewy; they're the family who moved into Kristy's house after the Thomases left it for Watson's mansion. The three Perkins girls are Myriah, who's five and a half, Gabbie Ann, who's two and a half, and Laura, the baby. Laura is so little that we usually don't take care of her, just Myriah and Gabbie. Right now, Laura pretty much goes wherever her mother goes.

Myriah and Gabbie are fun and us sitters like them a lot. The girls enjoy adventures and trying new things, which was why Mary Anne thought they'd like the trip to the Mancusis'. And they did like it. The awful-disgusting-gross-shivery-blechh thing had nothing to do with the girls. In fact, Mary Anne was the one who caused it. Myriah helped to solve it.

I better back up a little here. Okay, at about four o'clock on Tuesday afternoon I returned to the Mancusis' after walking the dogs, and found the phone ringing.

"Hello, Mancusi residence," I said breathlessly as I picked up the phone.

"Hi, Jessi, it's Mary Anne."

Mary Anne was calling to find out if she

could bring Myriah and Gabbie over. I told her yes, of course, and about twenty minutes later they showed up.

"Oh, boy! Aminals!" cried Gabbie. Her blonde hair was fixed in two ponytails that bobbed up and down as she made a dash for the Mancusis' kitchen.

"All kinds!" added Myriah. Myriah's hair was pulled back into one long ponytail that reached halfway down her back. She followed her sister.

The girls began exploring the house. The cats and dogs weren't too interesting to them since they've got one of each at their house — Chewy, and their cat, R.C. But the other animals fascinated them.

I showed them Barney. I showed them Lucy and Ricky. I explained everything I could think of to them. We moved on.

"These are — "

"Easter bunnies!" supplied Gabbie, as we looked in at Fluffer-Nut, Robert, Toto, and Cindy.

"You can hold them," I said. "The rabbits like to have a chance to get out of their hutch."

So Myriah held Toto, and Gabbie held Fluffer-Nut. For a few minutes, the girls had a giggle-fest. I looked around for Mary Anne.

When I didn't see her, I was relieved instead of worried. I didn't want to talk about Kristy or our club problems with her.

Soon the girls grew tired of the rabbits, so we put them back.

"Now these," I told Gabbie and Myriah, "are hamsters. Since they're sleeping, we won't disturb them. But see how fat that hamster's face is?" I pointed to one on top of the pile of hamsters. It was not the fat hamster. He was still off by himself in that corner of the cage. He seemed to have made a sort of nest. No, I pointed to one of the other hamsters.

"He looks like he has the mumps!" said Myriah.

"He does, doesn't he? But his fat cheeks are really — "

"AUGHHH!"

The scream came from the direction of the sun porch.

"Mary Anne?" I called.

"AUGHHH!" was her reply.

I put the lid back on the hamster cage, took Myriah and Gabbie by their hands, and ran with them to the sun porch.

A truly horrible sight met our eyes. We saw Barney's cage and the lid to Barney's cage — but no Barney.

"Mary Anne, what on earth happened?" I cried.

"Barney's loose!" was her response. "The *snake* is *loose!*"

Mary Anne and I got the same idea at the same time. We jumped up on one of the big porch chairs, the way people do when they've just seen a mouse.

Myriah and Gabbie looked at us as if we were crazy.

"What are you *do*ing?" exclaimed Myriah. "Barney's just a little snake. He can't hurt you. Besides, he could probably slither right up onto that chair. You can't escape him that way."

"Oh, EW!" shrieked Mary Anne.

"How did Barney get loose?" I asked her.

"Well, I'm not sure, but I think he just crawled out of his cage, or slithered out or whatever sn-snakes do. I — I mean, he did it after I forgot to put the lid back on his cage. I took it off so I could get a closer look at him, and then I heard someone saying, "Where's the beef? Where's the beef?" so I left to see who it was. And then I found the birds, and *then* I remembered Barney, and when I came back to replace the lid on his cage, he was gone. I am *so* sorry, Jessi."

"*Oh . . .*" I cried.

"Shouldn't we *find* Barney?" asked Myriah sensibly. "Before he gets too far away?"

"I guess so." I couldn't believe I was going to have to search for a snake. I couldn't think of anything stupider than searching for something you didn't want to find — or anything grosser than searching for a flicking tongue and a long, scaly body.

But it had to be done, and done fast.

"Let's split up," I suggested. "Barney probably couldn't have gotten upstairs, so we don't need to search there. Mary Anne, you and Gabbie look in the back rooms on this floor. Myriah and I will look in the front rooms."

"Okay," agreed Mary Anne, and we set off.

The search was a nightmare. Well, it was for Mary Anne and me. For Myriah and Gabbie it was like playing hide-and-seek with an animal. The odd thing was, I was so afraid of Barney that I was *less* worried about *not* finding him and having to tell the Mancusis he was lost than I was that we *would* find him. I went looking gingerly under chairs and tables and couches, always terrified that I'd come face to face with Barney and his flicking tongue.

But after twenty minutes of searching, there was no sign of Barney. And we'd been through every room on the first floor.

"Uh-oh," I said, as the four of us met in the hallway. "Now what? How am I going to tell the Mancusis that Barney is missing?"

"Long distance. It's the next best thing to being there!" called Frank from his cage.

We began to laugh, but then I said, "This is serious. We have to find Barney."

"Yeah," said Mary Anne. "Boy, am I sorry, Jessi. If — if you have to tell the Mancusis that . . . you know . . . I'll help you."

"Hey!" said Myriah suddenly. "I just thought of something. We're learning about animals in school, and Barney is a snake and snakes are reptiles and reptiles are cold-blooded. If I had cold blood, I'd want to warm up."

"Could Barney have gotten outside?" I said nervously. "Maybe he wanted sunshine. We might never find him outdoors, though."

"Well, let's look," said Mary Anne.

So we did. And we hadn't looked for long when Mary Anne let out another shriek.

"Where is he?" I cried, since I knew that was what her scream had meant.

"Here," she yelled. "On the back porch."

I ran around to the porch and there was Barney, napping peacefully in a patch of sunshine.

"You were right," I whispered to Myriah. "Thank you." Then I added, "How are we going to get him back in his cage, Mary Anne?"

Mary Anne looked thoughtful. "I have an idea," she said. "Do the Mancusis have a spare aquarium somewhere?"

I wasn't sure. We checked around and found one in the garage. It was empty but clean.

"Okay," said Mary Anne, "what we're going to do is put this aquarium over Barney. I'll — I'll do it, since I was the one who let him loose."

I didn't argue. The four of us returned to the porch, and Mary Anne crept up behind Barney, holding the overturned aquarium. She paused several feet from him. "I hope he doesn't wake up," she said.

Boy, I hoped he didn't, either.

Mary Anne tiptoed a few steps closer, then a few more steps closer. When she was about a foot away from him, she lowered the aquarium. Barney woke up — but not until the aquarium was in place.

"Now," said Mary Anne, "we slide a piece of really stiff cardboard under Barney. Then we carry him inside and dump him in his own cage. This is my spider-catching method. See, I don't like spiders, and I also don't like to squish them, so when I find one in the house, I trap it under a cup or a glass and take it outside."

Well, Mary Anne's suggestion was a good one. I found a piece of cardboard in a stack of newspapers the Mancusis were going to throw away. Mary Anne carefully slid it under Barney, the two of us carried him inside, Myriah opened his cage for us — and we dumped him in. I think Barney was relieved to be at home again.

Believe me, *I* was relieved to have him home. But if I'd known what was going to happen at our club meeting the next day, I would have thought that a snake on the loose was nothing at all.

CHAPTER 7

The Wednesday club meeting started off like most others, except that I actually arrived early! It was one of the first times ever. My work at the Mancusis' had gone quickly that day, and the dogs had behaved themselves, so I had reached Claudia's fifteen minutes before the meeting was to begin. I had even beaten Kristy.

"Hi, Claud!" I said when I entered her room.

"Hi, Jessi."

Claudia sounded sort of glum, but I didn't ask her about it. Her gloominess probably had something to do with the Kristy problem, and I wanted to stay out of that. So all I said was, "Neat shirt."

Claudia was wearing another of her great outfits. This one consisted of an oversized, short-sleeved cotton shirt with gigantic leaves printed all over it, green leggings — the same green as the leaves on her shirt — bright yellow push-down socks, her purple high-tops, and

60

in her hair a headband with a gigantic purple bow attached to one side.

Claud is so, so cool . . . especially compared to me. I was also wearing an oversized shirt — a white sweat shirt with ballet shoes on the front — but with it I was just wearing jeans and regular socks and regular sneakers. And honestly, I would have to do something about my hair soon. It looks okay when it's pulled back, I guess, but I want it to look special.

I sat down on the floor. Since no one else had arrived, I guess I could have sat on the bed, but Mallory and I just don't feel comfortable doing that. We're the youngest and we belong on the floor. Period.

I was about to ask Claud if she'd printed the leaves on her shirt herself, when Dawn burst into the room.

"Hi, you guys!" she said cheerfully. She tossed her long hair over one shoulder.

"Hi," replied Claudia. "You're in a good mood."

"I'm thinking positive," Dawn informed us. "Maybe it'll help the meeting along. . . . I mean, I *know* it will help the meeting. This meeting," she went on, "is going to be wonderful. There aren't going to be any prob . . ."

Dawn's voice trailed off as Kristy strode into club headquarters. Without so much as a word, she crossed the room to Claudia's bulletin board, pulled out a few thumbtacks, and posted a piece of paper right over a bunch of photographs of Claudia and Stacey.

Kristy turned to us and smiled. "There!" she announced proudly, as if she had just achieved world peace.

"There what?" said Claudia darkly.

"There's the checklist. I made it last night. It took forev — "

"And you put it up over my *pictures?!*" exclaimed Claudia. "Not on your life. Those are pictures of Stacey and me before she moved away." Claudia marched to the bulletin board and took the checklist down. She gave it back to Kristy. "Find another place for this, Ms. Bossy."

"Sheesh, I'm *sorry*, Claud," said Kristy. "I didn't know those picture were so important to you."

"Well, they are."

Personally, I thought Claud was overreacting a little. I guess Kristy thought so, too. The next thing I knew, she was tacking the checklist up over the photos again.

Claudia yanked it off.

Kristy put it back up.

Claudia yanked it off again. This time, the

checklist ripped. From one side hung a wrinkled strip.

Mallory and Mary Anne arrived just in time to hear Kristy let out a shriek and Claudia yell, "Leave this thing *off!* I don't want it on my bulletin board. I don't care how long it took you to make it!"

"Girls?" The gentle voice of Mimi, Claudia's grandmother, floated up the stairs. "Everything is okay?" (Mimi had a stroke last summer and it affected her speech. Sometimes her words get mixed up or come out funny.)

"YES!" Claudia shouted back, and I knew she didn't mean to sound cross. She lowered her voice. "Everything's fine, Mimi. Sorry about the yelling."

"That okay. No problem."

Claudia and Kristy were standing nose-to-nose by Claud's desk. They were both holding onto the checklist, and I could tell that neither planned to give it up. Not easily, anyway.

The rest of us were just gaping at them — Mallory and Mary Anne from the doorway, Dawn from the bed, and I from the floor.

"You," said Claudia to Kristy in a low voice, "are not the boss of this club."

Kristy looked surprised. Even I felt a little surprised. I don't think Kristy had meant to be bossy. She was just overexcited about her checklist.

But Kristy retorted, "I am the *president* of this club."

"Then," said Claudia, "it's time for new elections."

"*New* elections?" Kristy and Mallory and I squeaked.

"Yes," said a voice from the doorway. "New elections." It was Mary Anne.

Claudia and Kristy were so taken aback that they both let go of the checklist. It fell to the floor, forgotten.

Everyone turned to look at Mary Anne.

And then Mallory spoke up. Even though she's only a junior officer of the club, she's known for having a cool head in tough situations. So she took charge. "Everybody sit down," she said quietly. "In your regular seats. We have some things to straighten out. And we better calm down in case the phone rings."

As if Mal were psychic, the phone did ring then. We managed to schedule a job for the Barrett kids. By the time that was done, we had settled into our places. Kristy, in the director's chair, had even put her visor on.

"Okay," she began, "a motion has been made for . . . for . . ."

"New elections," supplied Claudia.

"All right. I'll consider the idea," said Kristy.

"No way," said Dawn, who, since the checklist war, had barely said a word. "You can't just consider the idea. Elections are our right. I *demand* new elections."

"Me too," said Mary Anne.

"Me too," said Claudia.

Mallory and I exchanged a worried glance. We were certain to be asked our opinion soon. And we were still trying to remain neutral.

Sure enough, Kristy looked down at Mal and me. I cringed. I knew she wanted us on her side. If we were, then the club would be divided three against three.

"Mallory, Jessi, what do you two think about the elections?" Kristy asked.

It would have been awfully nice to side with Kristy. Siding with the president is always nice. But I just couldn't. I didn't want to get involved in a club fight. I knew Mal didn't, either.

Since Mal wasn't speaking, I finally said, "What do we think about the elections?"

"Yes," said Kristy sharply.

"I . . . Well, I . . ." I shrugged. Then I looked helplessly at Mal.

"I — That's how . . . um . . ." was all Mallory managed to say.

"Do you want them?" Mary Anne asked us.

"Not that your positions would change, but you'd be voting."

Mallory and I did some more stammering. I think both of us felt that elections were a good idea, but neither of us wanted to admit it. Furthermore, a new worry was already creeping into my worry-laden mind. *How* would Mal and I vote in an election? If we voted to keep Kristy president, all the other club members would hate us. If we voted Kristy out, Kristy would hate us, and whether she was the president or the secretary, the club was still hers because she had dreamed it up and started it.

"Jessi? Mallory?" said Kristy again. We didn't even bother to answer, and suddenly Kristy threw down the pencil she'd been holding and exclaimed, "Okay, okay, okay. We'll have an election." I guess she could tell that no one was on her side. Jessi and I might not have been on the *other* side, but we weren't on hers, either.

"Good," said Claudia. "Well, we're ready."

"Not *now!*" cried Kristy as the phone rang.

We scheduled three jobs, and then Kristy went on, "I don't want to waste one of our regular meetings on elections. Besides, people call all the time during meetings."

"They call plenty of other times, too," Claud couldn't resist saying.

"Whatever," said Kristy. "Anyway, I'm calling a special meeting for the elections. Saturday afternoon at four o'clock. *This* meeting is adjourned."

"Whew," I said to Mallory when we were safely outside. "I don't like the sound of this."

"Me neither," agreed Mallory. "Not at all."

CHAPTER 8

On Thursday, I had help at the Mancusis'. Mallory came over so we could discuss the election problem, and Becca came over so she could play with the animals. The night before, she'd been so excited about the trip to the Mancusis' that she practically couldn't sleep. Nevertheless, she was a big help that afternoon, and so was Mallory.

Becca and I reached the Mancusis' about fifteen minutes before Mal did. I wanted to walk the dogs before I began feeding the animals, so we would have to wait for Mal to arrive. I used the time to introduce Becca to the animals.

"Come on," I said to her. "Come see the birds. You'll love them."

"Just a sec," replied Becca. She was lying on the floor, playing with Ling-Ling and Crosby, who were enjoying every second of her attention.

When Becca finally got to her feet, I led her back to Frank. I was just about to say, "This is Frank. Listen to what he can do," when Frank said, "The quicker picker-upper! The quicker picker-upper!"

Becca began to giggle. "That's great! How'd he learn to do that?"

"Watched too much TV, I guess. Like some people I know," I teased my sister.

"Oh, Jessi," replied Becca, but she was smiling.

"Try saying, 'Where's the beef?' " I suggested.

"Me?"

I nodded.

"Okay." Becca stood directly in front of Frank and said clearly, "Where's the beef? Where's the beef?"

"Long distance," replied Frank.

Becca and I laughed so hard that we didn't hear Mallory ring the doorbell until she was leaning on it for the third time.

"Oh! That's Mal!" I cried. "I'll be right back, Becca."

I dashed to the door and let Mal in.

"What took you so long?" she asked cheerfully. (Mal is usually cheerful.) "I rang three times."

I explained about Frank, and then, of course,

I had to show him to her. I led her back to Becca and the birds, and Becca promptly said, "Hi, Mallory. Listen to this. Hey, Frank, where's the beef? Where's the beef?"

"The quicker picker-upper!" Frank answered.

When we had stopped laughing, I said, "Come on, you guys. We've got to walk the dogs. Cheryl looks sort of desperate."

I took the leashes from the hooks and before I could even call the dogs, they came bounding into the kitchen.

"Okay, you guys. Ready for a walk?" I asked. (Dumb question. They were *dying* for a walk.)

I snapped their leashes on and they pulled me to the front door. "Come on!" I called to Becca and Mallory, who were still talking to Frank. "The dogs can't wait!"

Becca and Mallory clattered after me. As we ran through the doorway and down the steps, Mal asked, "Can we help you walk them? We could each take one leash."

"Thanks," I replied, "but I better do it myself. Besides, they're used to being walked together. You can hold onto them while I lock the door, though."

So Mallory took the leashes from me while I locked the Mancusis' door. Then she handed them back, and we set off down the street —

at a fast pace, thanks to Cheryl and her very long legs.

"Keep your eye on Pooh Bear," I told Becca and Mal. "She's the troublemaker."

"The little one?" exclaimed Becca.

"Yup," I said. "For instance, up ahead is . . . Oh, no, it's a cat! For a moment I thought it was just a squirrel, but a cat's worse. Pooh Bear might — OOF!"

Pooh Bear had spotted the cat, who was sunning itself at the end of a driveway. She jerked forward with a little bark, straining at the leash. Jacques spotted the cat next, and then Cheryl, although Cheryl doesn't care about cats. Anyway, the cat heard the barking, woke up, saw the dogs, and fled down the driveway.

"*Hold* it, you guys!" I yelled to the dogs. Pooh Bear and Jacques were practically dragging me down the street. Cheryl, too. She always likes a good run.

"We'll help you, Jessi!" I heard my sister cry. A few moments later, she and Mallory grabbed me around the waist. They pulled back so hard that the dogs stopped short, and all of us — dogs, Mal, Becca, and I — fell to the ground. When us humans began to laugh, the dogs started licking our faces.

It took several minutes to sort ourselves out

and stop laughing, but finally we were on our feet and walking again. Things went smoothly after that.

"I never knew dog-walking was so hard," commented Becca.

"It's only hard when you're walking Pooh Bear, Jacques, and Cheryl," I told her. "And when they're in the mood for cat-chasing."

We returned to the Mancusis' and I let the dogs inside and hung their leashes up. "Okay," I said, "feeding time."

"Puh-*lease* can I feed some of the animals?" begged Becca. "Even though it's your job? I'll be really good and careful."

"We-ell . . . okay," I said, relenting. "You have to follow instructions exactly, though, okay?"

"Yes, yes, yes! Okay!" Becca was so excited she began jumping up and down.

"All right. You can feed the guinea pigs, the rabbits, and the cats. Let me show you what to do."

I gave Becca instructions, and then Mal came with me while I fed the other animals. I started with the dogs because they absolutely cannot wait, and they are gigantic pains when they're hungry.

"Well," said Mallory, as I spooned dog food

into Cheryl's dish, "What do you think about the elections?"

I groaned. "Please. Do we have to talk about them?"

"I think we better."

"I know. You're right. I was just trying to . . . I don't know what. Oh well. Hey, Mal, you're not thinking of quitting, are you?" The idea had just occurred to me and it was an awful one, but if Mal and I refused to take sides, would we feel forced to quit the club?

"Thinking of quitting?!" exclaimed Mal. "No way. No one's going to get rid of me *that* easily. . . . But the meetings *are* pretty uncomfortable."

"I'll say," I agreed.

"And how are we going to vote Saturday?" wondered Mallory.

"Well, I guess," I began slowly. "Let me think. Okay, there are four offices — president, vice-president, secretary, and treasurer. And you and I are going to remain junior officers, so it'll be the same four girls running for the same four offices."

"Right," agreed Mallory.

I finished feeding the dogs, rinsed off the spoon I'd used, changed the water in their bowls, and moved onto the bird cages.

"Yesterday I was thinking," I told Mallory, "that if we vote Kristy out of her office — if we make her secretary or something — she'll be mad at us, which won't be good. I mean, I'll always think of the club as hers, whether she's president or not, because it was her idea and she started it. And I don't want her mad at us. On the other hand, if we vote for Kristy for president, all the other girls will be mad at us, and that won't be good, either. It almost doesn't matter how we vote for Mary Anne and Dawn and Claudia, but where Kristy is concerned, we lose either way."

"Wait a sec," Mal cut in. "Won't the voting be secret?"

"It should be, but even if it is, everyone will figure out who voted for whom. People always do."

"Oh, brother," said Mallory. "You're right. *And* I just thought of something even worse. If enough feelings are hurt by the voting, the club could *break up*. It really could. Then what?"

"I don't know," I said, heading for the hamster cage. "I hadn't even thought of that."

Mal and I peered in at the hamsters.

"Do they always sleep in a pile?" asked Mallory.

"Pretty much," I replied. "Except for that one. I pointed to the one in the corner. "He

74

sleeps by himself, and you know, I think he's fatter than he was a few days ago. I'm getting worried about him."

"Well, at least he's eating," said Mal.

"Maybe he's gotten too fat to move," I kidded, but I didn't try to smile at my joke. I was too worried. I was worried about the hamster, and worried about our special Saturday meeting.

Mal and Becca and I finished feeding the animals and changing their water. Becca played with the cats again and then it was time to leave.

"Good-bye, Cheryl! Good-bye, Ling-Ling!" Becca called. " 'Bye, Barney!' 'Bye, Fluffer-Nut!' 'Bye, Frank!' "

"Awk!" squawked Frank. "Tiny little tea leaves!"

CHAPTER 9

Thursday

I always look forward to sitting for Jackie Rodowsky, our walking disaster, even though he's more of a challenge than almost any other kid I can think of. Today was a challenge as usual, but it was a different kind of challenge. Jackie's having a tough time -- and I tried to help him with his problem. I'm not sure I did, though. In fact, I think I might have been bossing him around. I mean, I guess I was bossing him. Have I always done that? Or is it just lately? Well, anyway, Jackie was nice about it.

Kristy *might* have been bossing Jackie around? I'll say she bossed him! The good thing is that I think she learned something from Jackie. Let me start back at the beginning of the afternoon, though, when Kristy first arrived at the Rodowskys'.

Ding-dong.

"Rowf! Rowf-rowf!" Bo, the Rodowskys' dog, skidded to a halt at the door and waited for someone to come open it so he could see who was on the other side. A moment later, the door was opened by Jackie himself.

"Hi, Kristy," he said gloomily.

"Good afternoon, Eeyore," Kristy replied with a smile.

"Huh?" said Jackie.

"You look like Eeyore. You know, the sad donkey from *Winnie-the-Pooh*."

"Oh."

"What's wrong?"

"I'll tell you later. Come on in."

Kristy stepped inside. She took a good look at Jackie's sad face. He's got this shock of red hair and a faceful of freckles. When he grins, you can see that he's missing teeth (he's only seven), so he looks a little like Alfred E. Neuman from *Mad* magazine. You know,

77

"What, me worry?" But not that day. Jackie wasn't smiling.

"My brothers are at their lessons," Jackie informed Kristy, "Dad's at work, and Mom's going to a meeting."

Kristy nodded. That often happens. Jackie doesn't take any lessons because he's too accident-prone. He's our walking disaster. When Jackie's around, things just seem to happen. Vases fall, dishes break, earrings disappear. Things happen to Jackie, too. *He* falls or breaks things or loses things. Which is why he doesn't take lessons anymore. He tried to, but there were too many accidents when he was around.

Mrs. Rodowsky came downstairs then, and Kristy greeted her and listened to her instructions for the afternoon. Then Mrs. Rodowsky kissed Jackie good-bye and left.

"So," said Kristy, "what's up, Jackie? You look like you have a big problem."

Jackie nodded. "Yeah. I do."

"Do you want to tell me about it? I don't know if I could help, but I might have a couple of suggestions."

"Well," Jackie answered, "I could tell you, I guess. That won't hurt anything."

"Shoot," said Kristy.

Jackie heaved a huge sigh.

"Wait, let's make ourselves comfortable." Kristy led Jackie into the rec room and they settled themselves on the couch, Bo between them.

"Okay," said Kristy.

"All right. See, in my class," Jackie began, "our teacher said we were going to have elections." (Elections? thought Kristy.) "There are all kinds of neat things you can run for — blackboard-washer, messenger, roll-taker."

"Sounds like fun," said Kristy.

Jackie nodded. "That's what I thought. I wanted to run for the job of taking care of Snowball. He's our rabbit. That sounded like the funnest job of all." Jackie stopped talking and stroked Bo behind his ears.

"But?" Kristy prompted him.

"But there's no way I'm going to win."

"How come?"

" 'Cause I'm running against Adrienne Garvey. Adrienne is . . . is . . ." Jackie paused, thinking. "Well, she never erases holes into her workbook pages, and she never gets dirty, even in art class. And she always finishes her work on time. And she never forgets her lunch or trips or spills or *any*thing!"

"Ms. Perfect?" Kristy suggested.

"Yes," said Jackie vehemently. "And all the

other kids will vote for her. I just know it. They don't like Adrienne very much, but they know she'll do a good job. She'll never forget Snowball, and she'll keep his cage neat and stuff."

"What about you?"

"Me?" replied Jackie. "You mean, what kind of job would I do?"

Kristy nodded.

"Just as good as Adrienne!" Jackie cried. "Honest. I take good care of Bo, don't I, Bo?" (Bo whined happily.) "But, see, Bo's not mine. I mean, not just mine. He belongs to my brothers *and* me, so I don't take care of him everyday. And Snowball wouldn't be mine, either. He belongs to the whole class. But if I got the job, he would *feel* like mine since I would be the only one taking care of him. And I know I could do a good job. I know it."

"Then prove it to the kids in your class," said Kristy. "Show them that you'll be as neat and as responsible as Adrienne. Maybe even neater."

"And responsibler?"

Kristy smiled. "That, too."

"But how am I going to show them that?" wondered Jackie.

"Well, let's think it over."

"I — I could be neat myself," said Jackie after a few moments, sitting up straighter.

"That's a good start."

"And I could try to keep my workbook neat. And my desk neat."

"Even better."

Jackie paused, frowning.

"Do you think you can do those things?" asked Kristy.

" 'Course I can!" To prove his point, Jackie jumped to his feet. "Watch me neaten up," he cried, and then added, "I did this once before, for a wedding. . . . Okay, buttons first." Jackie's shirt was buttoned wrong, so that on top an extra button stuck up under his chin, and on the bottom one shirttail trailed an inch or two below the other.

Jackie unfastened the first button — and it came off in his hands.

"Uh-oh," he said, but his usual cheerfulness was returning. "Um, Kristy, if you could . . . whoops." Another button came off.

"Here," said Kristy, "let me do that for you."

"No," said Jackie, "I have to learn to —"

Too late. Kristy was already unbuttoning and rebuttoning Jackie's shirt. "There you go," she said. "Now the next thing I think you should do is start a campaign—you know, slogans, speeches, that sort of thing."

"But *I*," Jackie replied, "think I should practice filling Bo's dish neatly. It's almost time to feed him anyway."

"Well," said Kristy reluctantly, "okay." She was thinking that she really wanted to help Jackie win the election for the job of Snowball-Feeder. But she was also thinking that Jackie plus a bag of dog food equals big trouble. However, if Jackie believed that feeding Bo would help him, then Kristy would go along with his idea.

"Where's Bo's food?" Kristy asked.

"It's — Oh, I just remembered. We used up a bag yesterday. We have to start a new one. Mom keeps them in the basement."

Kristy cringed. Jackie was going to carry a bag of dog food from the basement up to the rec room and then up to the kitchen? "Be careful," she called after him.

Jackie disappeared into the basement. A moment later, Kristy heard his feet on the stairs. "I'm coming!" Jackie announced. "And I'm being careful!"

Jackie reached the rec room safely.

He grinned at Kristy.

He headed up the stairs to the kitchen.

Halfway there, the bottom of the bag gave

out. Dog food cascaded down the stairs into the rec room.

Jackie looked at Kristy in horror. Then he smacked his forehead with the heel of his hand. "I did it again!" he exclaimed. His face began to crumple.

"Oh, Jackie," said Kristy, eyeing the mess. "Don't cry. It wasn't your fault." She wanted to reach out and give him a hug, but a sea of kibbles lay between them.

Jackie stood miserably on the steps. "I *know* it wasn't my fault," he cried.

"It couldn't have been," agreed Kristy. "The glue on the bottom of the bag must have come undone."

"But that's just it!" Jackie replied. "Don't you see? It came undone while *I* was holding it. Not Mom. Not Dad. Not my brothers. Not the man at the grocery store. Me. I'm bad luck. Maybe that's why the kids at school don't want me feeding Snowball."

"Then make the kids forget about your bad luck," suggested Kristy.

"How?"

"Campaigning. I'll help you with it as soon as we put this food into another bag."

"All right," said Jackie, but he didn't sound very enthusiastic.

Kristy found a garbage bag and the two of

them swept the kibbles into it. When nothing was left on the stairs but kibble dust, Kristy got out the Dustbuster.

"Let me do that," said Jackie.

"No, *I'll* do it." Kristy wasn't about to let Jackie touch an appliance. "Okay," she said a few minutes later, as she switched the Dustbuster off, "let's plan your campaign."

Jackie found a pencil and a pad of paper. He and Kristy sat down on the couch again, but Jackie immediately got up.

"Forgot to feed Bo," he said. "See? I am responsible. I remember to take care of animals." He ran upstairs, fed Bo, and returned to the couch without a single accident.

"All right," said Kristy, "now what I think you should do—"

"Kristy?" Jackie interrupted. "Can I tell you something?"

"Sure."

"I like you, but you're an awful bossy babysitter. You buttoned my shirt when I wanted to do it myself, you wouldn't let me vacuum up the mess I made, and now you're going to plan my campaign for — Whoops."

Jackie had dropped his pencil into a heating grate. He and Kristy had to scramble around in order to get it out. In the excitement, Jackie forgot about what he'd said to Kristy. But Kristy didn't. It was all she could think of later as she helped Jackie with his campaign — and tried very hard not to be too bossy.

Was she really a bossy person?

CHAPTER 10

I was scared to go to the Friday meeting of the Baby-sitters Club.

Isn't that silly? I really was afraid, though, so while I was at the Mancusis' feeding the animals and worrying about the hamster, I phoned Mal.

"Hi," I said. "It's me."

"Hi, Jessi. Where are you?"

"At the Mancusis'. I'm almost done, though. Um, I was wondering. You want me to come by your house so we can walk to the meeting together?"

"Are you scared, too?"

Now this is what I love about Mallory. I suppose it's why we're best friends. We know each other inside out, and we're always honest with each other. Mal knew I was scared. And she admitted that she was scared. She could easily just have said, "Are you scared?" but she said, "Are you scared, *too?*" which is very important.

"Yeah, I am," I told her.

"Well, *please* stop by. I'd feel much better."

So of course I stopped by. Mallory and I walked to Claudia's with our arms linked, as if we could fend off arguments and yelling and hurt feelings that way.

We had to unlink our arms at the Kishis' front door, though. It was the only way to get inside.

Mimi greeted us in the hallway.

"Who's here?" I asked her.

I must have looked scared because she answered, "All others. But do not worry, Jessi. I know plobrems will . . . will work out."

I nodded. "Thanks, Mimi."

Mal and I climbed the stairs as slowly and as miserably as if we were going to our own funerals. We walked down the hallway. I heard only silence. I threw a puzzled glance back to Mallory, who shrugged.

A few more seconds and I was standing in Claudia's doorway. Well, there was the reason for the silence. Everyone was present all right, but no one was talking — not to Kristy, not to each other.

Mary Anne was sitting stiffly on the end of

Claudia's bed. She was gazing at the ceiling; her eyes looked teary.

Claudia, at the other end of her bed, was leafing silently through one of her sketchbooks.

Dawn was seated between Mary Anne and Claudia, and her long hair was falling across her face, almost as if she hoped to hide from everyone by not being able to see them.

And Kristy, well, Kristy looked like she always looks. She was poised in the director's chair, her visor in place, a pencil over one ear. I couldn't read the expression on her face, though.

Oops, I thought, as I paused in the doorway. If I stand here too long, Kristy will say, "What's with you guys? Are you going to stand there all day? Come on in so we can get started."

But Kristy didn't say a word. She just glanced at Mal and me and gave us a little smile. So we crept into Claudia's room and settled ourselves on the floor.

Kristy waited another minute until the digital clock on Claud's desk read 5:30. That minute was the longest one of my life. I was dying to whisper something to Mal like, "This room feels like a morgue," or, "Calm down, everybody. You're too cheerful. You're going to get out of control." But I couldn't. For one thing, in all that silence, everyone would have heard what I said. For another, I think the girls kind of *wanted* to feel bad, and I wasn't about to be responsible for cheering them up.

"Order," said Kristy as the numbers on the clock switched from 5:29 to 5:30.

Everyone already was in order.

"Well, um, is there any club business?" asked Kristy.

No one said a word. No one even moved.

Since it wasn't Monday, there were no dues to be collected, and Kristy didn't need to ask if we'd read the notebook. (Not that she'd bring it up. I had a feeling "notebook" was going to be a dirty word for awhile.)

Kristy cleared her throat. "Well," she said in this falsely cheerful voice, "any snacks, Claud?"

Silently Claudia reached behind the pillows on her bed and pulled out a bag of Doritos and a bag of popcorn. She passed the Doritos to Dawn and the popcorn to Kristy. The bags circled the room in opposite directions. No one reached into the bags. No one took so much as a kernel of popcorn, not even Kristy, who had asked about food in the first place.

I guess that had just been something for Kristy to say, that she wasn't really hungry.

And that was when I realized that she — our president, our queen — was as uncomfortable as the rest of us were.

Ring, ring.

Thank heavens. A phone call. I had never been more relieved to hear that sound. Like robots, Dawn answered the phone and Mary Anne scheduled a job for Claudia with the Marshall girls.

Ring, ring.

Another call came in. Then another and another.

At about 5:50, the phone stopped ringing, and Kristy, looking more uncomfortable than ever, said, "All right. I — I have a few things to say about the elections tomorrow."

"We're still going to have them, aren't we?" asked Claudia.

"Of course. But I wanted to figure out a way to avoid ties in the voting. This is what I came up with. First of all, Jessi and Mallory, you'll be voting, as you know."

We nodded.

"There are two reasons for that," Kristy continued. "One, you're club members, so you *should* vote. Two, we need five people voting in order to prevent a lot of ties. I know that sounds confusing, but you'll see what I mean in a few minutes."

"Okay," Mal and I said at the same time.

"Next, the voting will be secret. I'll make up ballots with boxes by our names. All we'll have to do is write X's in the boxes. I don't think we can get much more secret than that."

Stony silence greeted Kristy. I frowned. Wasn't anyone else relieved to hear what she'd just said?

Kristy continued anyway. "The last thing," she said, "is that, you, Mary Anne, you, Claudia, you, Dawn, and I—the four of us— will be able to vote in the election for each office except the one we hold. In other words, I can vote in the elections for vice-president, secretary, and treasurer, but not president. The reason for this is that without me, for instance, five people will be choosing from among four people for president. A tie is possible, but not likely. I think we'll avoid a lot of revotes this way."

"Anything else?" asked Dawn from behind her hair.

"No, that about covers it."

"I'll say it does," snapped Claudia.

"What's that supposed to mean?" Kristy replied.

Yeah, I wondered. What *is* that supposed to mean?

"Can I answer?" spoke up Mary Anne. Her

voice was wobbling ever so slightly.

"Be my guest," said Claudia.

Mary Anne drew in a deep breath, probably to control her voice. "Kristy," she began, "have you ever heard of a democracy?"

Sensing an argument, Kristy replied sarcastically, "Why, no. I never have. What is a democracy, Mary Anne?"

Mary Anne tried hard to ignore the tone of Kristy's voice. "In a democracy," she said, "everyone has a say — "

"Which is why we're holding elections," Kristy interrupted, "and why we're all voting in them."

"I don't believe it," Dawn muttered. "She did it again."

"Kristy, would you listen to Mary Anne, please?" said Claudia.

Kristy rolled her eyes. Then she turned her gaze on Mary Anne and waited.

"In a democracy," Mary Anne began again, "everyone has a say in running the country. This club should be a democracy, too, Kristy, and the members should have a say in running things. In other words, you should have consulted us about the voting — about the ballots and the way the elections will be run."

Kristy blushed. I really thought she was going to apologize, but Dawn cut her off.

"But *nooooo*," Dawn said sarcastically. "You just barge ahead and do whatever seems right to you. You, you, you. You never think of what other people might want or feel."

It is not a good idea to make absolute statements like that — you *never*, *no one* does, *everybody* does. I have learned this the hard way. If I say to my mother, "But Mama, *everyone* is wearing them," she'll reply, "*Every*one? Your grandfather? Squirt?" You know, that sort of thing.

So naturally Kristy pounced on the "you never think" part of what Dawn had said. "I *never* think of other people? What about when Claudia broke her leg and wanted to quit the club. Didn't I help her through that? I even helped her figure out what was wrong. And what about — "

"But Kristy," said Mary Anne in a small voice, "so many times you just don't think. You just don't . . . " Mary Anne's wavery voice finally broke and she burst into tears.

Dawn jumped to her feet. "Oh, that is nice, Kristy. That is really nice. Now look what you did."

"Look what *I* did?! I didn't do that! Mary Anne cries all the time. She does it by herself."

Dawn didn't answer. She walked out of Claudia's room in a huff.

"Be back here at four o'clock tomorrow," Kristy shouted after her. She looked at the rest of us. "You, too," she added. "This meeting is adjourned."

Mary Anne didn't move from her place on the bed, and Claud edged toward her, looking sympathetic. Mallory and I waited for Kristy to leave. Then we left, too. We walked slowly down the stairs.

When we were outside, I said, "Well, was the meeting as bad as you thought it would be?"

"Yup," replied Mallory. "How about you?"

"Worse. It was worse. Do you have a good feeling about tomorrow?"

"Not really. Do you?"

"No. Well, 'bye, Mal."

"'Bye, Jessi."

CHAPTER 11

On Saturday morning I woke up with butterflies in my stomach. I felt just like I do on the morning of a dance recital. Nervous, nervous, nervous. What on earth would happen at the special meeting that afternoon? I lay in bed and worried.

It was funny. I'd only been living in Stoneybrook, Connecticut, for a few months, but the Baby-sitters Club had become extremely important to me. Maybe that was because it was the first place here, besides Mallory's house, where I'd felt completely accepted; where I'd felt it truly didn't matter that I'm black.

If the club were to break up — if the girls were to get so mad at each other that they decided not to continue it — what would happen? I knew I'd still have Mallory, and I knew I'd still be friendly with the other girls, but it wouldn't be the same. Not to mention that I *love* baby-sitting and I'd miss all the jobs I get through the club.

I heaved a deep sigh, trying to make the butterflies in my stomach calm down. I rolled over. At last I sat up. Maybe, I thought, if I stay in bed I can make time stop, and four o'clock will never arrive. Unfortunately, I'm too old to believe in things like that anymore.

I got out of bed, put some clothes on, and went downstairs. But I didn't go into the kitchen for breakfast. Instead, I checked my watch, decided it wasn't too early for a phone call, and dialed Mallory's number.

I sprawled on the couch in the den.

"Hello?" said a small voice on the other end of the phone.

"Hi . . . Claire?" (The voice sounded like Mallory's five-year-old-sister.)

"Yeah. Is this Jessi?"

"Yup. How are you?"

"Fine. I lost a tooth! And guess what — after *I* lost it, the *Tooth Fairy* lost it."

"She did? How do you know?"

"'Cause I found some money under my pillow and I found the tooth on the floor. The Tooth Fairy must have dropped it after she left the money."

I managed not to laugh. "I guess even the

Tooth Fairy makes mistakes," I said to Claire. "Listen, can I talk to Mallory, please?"

"Sure," answered Claire. "Mallory-silly-billy-goo-goo! Phone for you!"

A few moments later, I heard Mallory's voice. "Hello?"

"Hi, it's me."

"Hi, Jessi. How long did you have to talk to Claire?"

"Just for a few minutes."

"That's good. She's in one of her silly moods, in case you couldn't tell."

I laughed. Then, "So," I said, "are you ready for this afternoon?"

"I hope so."

"What do you think is going to happen?"

"You know, I really don't have any idea."

"Do you know who you're going to vote for?" I asked.

"I've been trying not to think about it," Mal told me. "And I tried so hard that I really haven't thought about it, and now I don't know who to vote for."

"Oh. I just don't know who to vote for, period."

Mal sighed.

I sighed.

"Well," I said finally, "I better get going. I

have a lot to do before the meeting. The Mancusis come home tomorrow, so today I want to make sure everything is perfect at their house. I've got to walk the dogs and feed the animals as usual, but I also want to clean out some of the cages, change the litter in the cats' box, that sort of thing."

"Okay. Will you come by for me again this afternoon? It'd be nice to walk to the meeting together," said Mallory.

"Sure," I replied. "I'll see you around quarter to four."

We said good-bye and hung up, and then I wandered into the kitchen, where I found my mother and Squirt. "'Morning," I said.

"'Morning, honey."

"Where are Daddy and Becca?"

"Your father went into the office for the morning, and Becca's gone over to Charlotte's house."

I nodded. I sat down in front of Squirt's high chair and made faces at him. "Mama?" I said after awhile.

My mother looked up from the recipe card she was reading. "Yes, honey? Aren't you going to eat breakfast this morning? Everyone else has eaten already."

"I'll eat," I replied, "but I have to ask you about something first."

Mama could tell it was important. She sat down next to me at the table. "What is it, honey?"

As best I could, I explained to her what was going on in the Baby-sitters Club. I told her everything — how Kristy can be bossy sometimes, that the other girls are upset, and what might happen at the elections that afternoon.

"Go-bler?" said Squirt from his high chair. He was playing with a set of plastic keys and two red rings.

"Jessi," said Mama, "I think you want me to tell you how to vote, don't you?"

"Well, yes," I answered. "I mean, even just a hint or something."

"But I can't give you answers. You have to make up your own mind. I will give you one piece of advice, though."

"Okay."

"Vote for the person you honestly think is best suited for each office. Don't worry about anything else."

"All right. Thanks, Mama."

I ate my breakfast, feeling somewhat let down. My mother always has the answers. Why couldn't she tell me who to vote for? But I knew there was no point in asking her again. I would just have to figure things out for myself, and I would have plenty of time to think while I worked at the Mancusis'.

The first thing I did was walk Pooh Bear, Cheryl, and Jacques. It was late morning and the dogs were frantic to get outside. I snapped their leashes on and led them to the front door. As soon as it was opened a crack, Pooh Bear pushed her way through. The dogs tried to bound across the front lawn while I was still trying to lock the Mancusis' door.

"Hold on!" I yelled.

I locked the door, and the dogs pulled me to the street. We took a wild walk, racing past people, bicycles, and mailboxes. At last the dogs slowed down, and I relaxed a little.

I decided to think about the elections. I would consider one office at a time, starting with treasurer. Dawn, I thought, made a good treasurer. She always collected our dues, she always remembered to pay Charlie, she always let us know when the treasury was getting low. But if she didn't like the job, then . . . well, Claudia certainly couldn't be treasurer. She's terrible at math. Mary Anne's okay at it, but she was so good as secretary. That left Kristy. Somehow, I just couldn't see her as treasurer of the Baby-sitters club.

This isn't getting me anywhere, I thought as I walked the dogs back to the Mancusis'.

I decided to try a different office. Vice-president. Claudia really was the perfect vice-president, what with her own phone and her own phone number. But, okay, she was tired of the job. So let's see. Kristy could be our vice-president, but how was she going to answer all the calls that come in at nonmeeting times? She couldn't. Not unless we moved club headquarters to her house. Maybe she could ask her mother and stepfather for her own phone. . . . That sounded like an awful lot of trouble to go to, just to switch offices in the club.

I couldn't solve that problem, so I put the election dilemma aside while I tended to the animals. I let the dogs back in the house and fed them. Then I changed their water. They ate quickly (and messily) and ran off. I cleaned up their area of the kitchen.

Then I moved on to the cats. Since they were in the living room, sleeping, I cleaned up their dishes and placemats first. I set their food out. I cleaned their litter box, found the Mancusis' Dustbuster, and vacuumed up the stray kitty litter that was strewn across the floor.

I worked very hard. I took care of the birds

and the bird cage, the rabbits and their hutch, and the fish and aquarium.

Time for the hamsters. I leaned over and peered into their cage. The fat one in the corner suddenly woke up and looked back at me with bright eyes.

"Why are you all alone?" I asked him. I stuck my finger in the cage, intending to stroke the hamster, but he lunged for me. I pulled my hand back just in time. "Whoa! What's wrong with you?" I exclaimed. I paused. I realized I had just said, "What's wrong with you?" A cold feeling washed over me. Something *was* wrong with the hamster. Maybe he had broken a bone. Maybe that's why he didn't want to be with the others and why he was bad-tempered.

Whatever was wrong had been wrong all week. It had been wrong since the Mancusis left, maybe even before that. The Mancusis hadn't noticed for some reason, but I had. I'd noticed right away. Why hadn't I done anything about it? What would the Mancusis think if they came back and I pointed out the hamster, saying he'd been sick or hurt all week, and then admitted that I hadn't done anything for him? That certainly wasn't very responsible. If I were baby-sitting and one of the kids got sick or broke a bone, I'd call his parents or his doctor or an ambulance. Well, I certainly wasn't going to call the Mancusis long distance about a maybe-sick hamster . . . but I could take the hamster to the vet.

I grabbed the phone and dialed my number. My mother answered.

"Mama!" I cried. "One of the hamsters is very sick. He sleeps in the corner by himself, and he's getting fatter and fatter, and just now he almost bit me. I think he might have a broken bone. Anyway, I noticed something was wrong last weekend and I don't know why I didn't do anything, but I didn't, and — "

"Jessi, honey, slow down," Mama broke in. "What do you want to do?"

"Take the hamster to the vet. Can you drive me?"

"Of course. Bring the address of the vet with you. And give me a few minutes to get Squirt ready. Your father's still at work. Oh, and please be careful with the hamster, especially since he's biting."

"Okay," I replied, calming down a little. "Thanks, Mama. You know which house is the Mancusis', don't you?"

Mama said she did, so we got off the phone. I was just about to figure out how we were going to take the hamster to the vet, when something occurred to me. I looked at my watch. Two-thirty. The special meeting of the Baby-sitters Club was supposed to start in an hour and a half.

I would never make it.

CHAPTER 12

I couldn't worry about the meeting, not just then, anyway. I had to get the hamster ready for the trip to the vet. What could I carry him in? I ran into the Mancusis' garage and found a stack of cardboard boxes. Among them was a shoe box. Perfect, I thought.

I filled the shoe box with shavings and carried it inside. Then I had to figure out how to get the hamster into the shoe box. I didn't want to touch him in case he was hurting. Finally I cleaned out an empty dog-food can, made sure there were no rough edges, placed some treats in it, put it in the hamster cage right next to the fat hamster — and he crawled in! Then I moved the can into the box. We were all set.

The hamster crawled back out of the can and quickly settled down in the box. He didn't try to get out. Even so, I punched some holes in the lid of the box, planning to bring it with me. You never know what might happen, so it's always best to be prepared.

Beep, beep.

That must be Mama, I thought.

I grabbed the box and my jacket and went outside, being careful not to jostle the box. The Mancusis' house key was in my pocket. I remembered to lock their front door.

"Thanks, Mama!" I cried, as I slid into the front seat of her car.

Behind me, Squirt was strapped into his car seat. He was babbling away.

"Let's see this little guy," said Mama.

I removed the lid and held out the box.

"He seems quiet," commented Mama, "but — "

"He's been just like this all week," I interrupted her.

"Okay, then. We better be on our way. Where's the Mancusis' vet?"

I gave her the address. Then I sat back. I felt relieved just to be doing something.

"Broo-broo-broo-broo," sang Squirt as we drove along.

We pulled into the parking lot of the veterinary offices, and I put the lid back on the box. No telling what we would find when we got inside. Well, it was a good thing I did. The waiting room was a madhouse. Mama stepped out of the car carrying Squirt and a bunch of his toys, and I stepped out with the hamster in the box. When I opened the door to the vet's office I was surprised. I'd never been to a vet because we've never had a pet, so I don't know what I thought the waiting room would be like, but . . .

For starters, it was noisy. Most of the people were sitting there with dogs or cats. The cats were safely in carrying cases, except for a Siamese on a leash. And they were fairly quiet, but two cats — the Siamese and a tabby cat — were yowling loudly. And plenty of the dogs were barking; the little ones with high, sharp yips, the big ones with deep rowfs.

Squirt looked around, taking in the people and animals, and listening to the noise, and his lower lip began to tremble.

Mama patted him on the back. It's okay, Mr. Squirt,'' she said. ''It's just a lot of — ''

Suddenly my mother let out a shriek. She pointed at something across the room. I looked and saw it, too.

It was a snake. And not just a little garter snake like Barney, either. Some great big kind of snake was draped around the neck of a boy who looked as if he were about fourteen years old.

''Oh, my . . .'' my mother started to say.

She looked like she might faint, so I tried to

figure out how to catch both her and Squirt without squishing the hamster, if she did.

But she didn't. Thank goodness.

And from across the room the boy said politely, "Don't worry. He's just a boa constrictor. He's not poisonous or anything. Sorry he scared you."

My mother smiled at him, but headed for seats as far from the boy as possible. She sat Squirt safely in her lap. "All right, honey," she said to me, "you better go tell the receptionist about your hamster and explain why you don't have an appointment."

"Okay." I carried the hamster across the waiting room, skirting around the boy with the snake, and stepped up to the desk. I placed the box on the desk and opened it.

"Yes?" said the receptionist.

"Hi," I began. "My name is Jessi Ramsey. I'm pet-sitting for the Mancusis this week and one of their hamsters is sick."

"Oh, the Mancusis," said the woman. She seemed to remember the name. I realized that with all their animals, they must have to go to the vet fairly often. "What seems to be the trouble?"

"Well, it's just that he doesn't sleep with the other hamsters and he's very bad-tempered."

108

I edged the box forward and the woman peered in at the hamster.

"Fat, isn't he?" she commented.

"Yes," I replied. "In fact, he's fatter than he was a week ago. I think maybe he's in pain. Something just doesn't seem right."

The woman nodded. "Okay. If you're worried, it's better to have things checked out. I have to tell you, though, that because you don't have an appointment, and because this isn't an emergency, you might have a long wait. It's hard to tell. There are five doctors in today, which is a lot, but there are also a lot of animals waiting."

"That's okay," I told her. "Just as long as he gets checked." I started to stroke the hamster's head before I replaced the lid on the box, but thought better of it. Then I made my way back to Mama.

I was beginning to feel awfully nervous. I checked my watch. Two forty-five. A quarter to three. Our special meeting would start in a little over an hour. Could I possibly make it? Was there any way?

I sat down next to Mama and tried hard not to bite my nails.

Then Squirt leaned over from his place on Mama's lap and said, "Pockita?" which is his way of asking to play patty-cake. We played patty-cake until a girl about Becca's age came into the waiting room with her father. She was holding a kitten, and she headed for the empty seats next to Mama. Her father spoke to the receptionist.

"What an adorable kitten," said my mother as the girl settled herself in a seat.

Immediately the girl stood up again. "Her name is Igga-Bogga," she said. She offered Igga-Bogga to us, and Mama and I took turns holding her, while Squirt patted her.

Igga-Bogga was skinny. And she was pure white, not a patch or a stripe or even a hair of another color anywhere. If she were my cat, I would have named her Misty or Clouds or Creampuff.

I was about to mention those names to the girl, when she spoke up again. "Guess what. It's so sad. Igga-Bogga is deaf."

"Deaf!" I cried.

The girl nodded. "That happens sometimes with white cats."

Her father joined us and he and Mama began talking about white cats being deaf. I looked at my watch. Three-ten. Less than an hour until the special meeting. What could I do? The hamster was my responsibility, my sitting responsibility. If I were baby-sitting on a weekday afternoon and the parents didn't come home and I had a club meeting to go to — well, I'd just have to miss the meeting, wouldn't I? Sitting responsibilities come first. So right now, a sick hamster came first.

I knew I was right, yet I started tapping my fingers and jiggling my feet. Oh, I *hate* being late and missing events I'm supposed to go to, and I *especially* hate upsetting Kristy.

"Miss Ramsey?" It was the receptionist.

My head snapped up. "Yes," I said. "I'm right here."

I picked up the hamster and his box and got to my feet. Next to me, Mama gathered up Squirt and his toys.

I checked my watch for the umpteenth time. Three-thirty! How did it get to be three-thirty? I would have to call Kristy as soon as I could safely step out of the doctor's office.

A nurse led Mama and Squirt and me through a doorway, down a corridor, and into an examining room.

"Hi, there. I'm Doctor West," said a friendly looking man wearing a white lab coat. He stuck his hand out.

Mama and I shook it, and I introduced us.

"So you've got one of the Mancusi pets here?" said Dr. West when the introductions were over. "Let me take a look."

While Dr. West examined the hamster, I ducked into the waiting room to use the pay phone I'd seen there. First I called Kristy.

". . . so I'm not going to be able to make the meeting," I finished up after I'd told her the story. "I'm really sorry."

"No problem," Kristy replied easily. "You did the right thing."

"I did?" I said. "Even though it's a hamster?"

"The hamster is your sitting charge," said Kristy. "Pets, kids, it doesn't matter. You're being responsible. That's what matters."

"Thanks, Kristy."

"Listen, I'll call the others and tell them the meeting has been postponed. We'll try to arrange it for eleven o'clock tomorrow morning, but call me tonight to check on the time."

"Okay," I said. "Thanks again, Kristy."

I hung up the phone, then dropped in another coin and called Mal to explain why I wouldn't be stopping by her house to pick her up.

When that was done, I returned to Dr. West's office. I found him and my mother grinning.

"What?" I said. "Why are you smiling?"

"Because," answered Mama, "your hamster isn't a he, he's a she. And *she* is pregnant!"

"I'd say she's going to have her babies within the next twenty-four hours," added Dr. West.

"You were lucky you didn't touch her today. A pregnant hamster should not be handled." Dr. West instructed me to transfer the other hamsters to a separate cage so the mother could be alone with her babies after giving birth. "And don't handle her at all," he said again. "A pregnant hamster is very delicate. Put her back in her cage by lowering the box inside it and letting her crawl out."

"Okay," I replied. Then I thanked Dr. West.

I rode back to the Mancusis' in high spirits. "Just think," I said to Mama. "The hamster is a girl, not a boy, and she's going to have babies! I'll have to give her a name. I want to be able to call her something."

Mama dropped me off and Squirt waved to me from the car window."

"Good-bye!" I called. " 'Bye, Squirt. Thank you for helping me, Mama. I'll be home as soon as I walk the dogs again and do the afternoon chores."

Mama beeped the horn as she drove down the street.

I ran to the Mancusis' garage before I did anything else. There I found the aquarium we had used to capture Barney. I poured shavings into it and added some food and a spare water bottle, and gently moved the hamsters into it. Then, even more gently, I set the shoe box in the old cage and let the pregnant hamster crawl out.

"What should I call you?" I asked aloud as she settled into her nest in the corner of the cage. "Maybe Suzanne. I always liked that name. . . . No. Suzanne is dumb for a hamster. Chipper? Nah, too cute. And it sounds like a boy's name. Sandy? You are sand-colored. Nah, that's boring. After lots of thinking, I decided to call her Misty, which is what I would name a white kitten if I had one. The hamster wasn't anywhere near white, but I decided that didn't matter. Misty was a good name.

I went home feeling excited. When I came back in the morning, Misty would be a mother!

CHAPTER 13

Sunday morning I woke up super-early. I had a lot to do at the Mancusis' before I left for Claudia's. I had to walk the dogs, feed the dogs and cats, and finish the chores I had begun the day before. And of course I wanted to check on Misty and her babies.

I ran straight for Misty as soon as I'd closed the Mancusis' door behind me. When I reached the kitchen, though, I slowed down and tiptoed inside. I peeked into Misty's cage.

Nothing.

Just Misty and her nest and a pile of shavings.

"Oh, you didn't have them yet," I said, feeling disappointed. I began to wonder if Dr. West had been wrong. Then what? Well, the Mancusis would be home in the afternoon. I would tell them the story and let them decide what to do. At least Misty had been to a doctor.

Besides, worrywart, I told myself, Dr. West said the babies would be born in the next twenty-four hours. There were about seven more hours to go until the twenty-four were up.

So I left Misty to herself, walked the dogs, fed them and the cats, finished the cleaning, and then . . . took off for our special club meeting. I dropped by Mallory's house on the way, since we were still planning to arrive at Claudia's together.

Mallory was waiting on her porch steps. "Hi!" she called when she spotted me.

"Hi," I replied.

Mallory ran across her front lawn. "Did the hamster have her babies yet?" she asked breathlessly. (I'd told Mal everything the night before.)

I shook my head. "Not yet. I wish she had. I wanted her to have them before the Mancusis get back."

"Maybe we could check on her after the meeting," suggested Mal.

"Oh! That's a good idea. We could *all* come."

Mal made a face at the thought, but the only thing she said was, "Do you know who you're going to vote for?"

I nodded my head slowly. "I think so. I probably won't know for sure until I'm actually voting, but right now I *think* I know."

"Funny," said Mal. "I feel the same way. . . .

Should we say who we're going to vote for?"

"No," I replied. "Better not. We should go ahead with what we've planned on. If we say anything, we might change each other's minds."

"Okay."

A few more minutes and Mal and I had reached the Kishis' house. We looked at each other.

"Dum da-dum dum," sang Mal ominously.

I laughed — or tried to.

Mal opened the door. We went inside and straight up to Claud's room. Kristy was already there, busily sorting through some slips of paper.

"Hi, you guys," Claud greeted us.

"Hi," we replied, settling into our places on the floor.

"What — " Claud started to say, but she was interrupted by the arrival of Mary Anne and Dawn, both looking a little sleepy.

When everyone was sitting in her usual spot, Kristy surprised us by beginning the meeting with, "Tell us about the hamster, Jessi."

I jerked to attention. I'd been preparing for the voting. Now I had to switch gears. "Well," I said, "this is good news. The hamster isn't sick — "

"Oh, that's wonderful!" cried Dawn. "So it was a false alarm?"

117

"Not exactly," I answered. "The hamster turns out to be a she. By the way, I'm calling her Misty for the time being. And Misty is . . ." (I looked at Mal, dragging out the suspense.)

"Yes?" shrieked Mary Anne.

" . . . Going to have babies!" I exclaimed. "Probably lots of them. Doctor West said hamsters usually give birth to six to twelve young. Those were his exact words. And it should happen any minute now, because yesterday afternoon he said it would happen within the next twenty-four hours."

"That is so exciting!" squealed Dawn.

"Babies!" exclaimed Mary Anne.

"Lots of them!" added Claudia.

"The Mancusis will be thrilled!" cried Kristy.

For a moment, I felt as if I were in a regular club meeting, back before we had started fighting all the time. Then Kristy said, "When the meeting is over, maybe we could go to the Mancusis' and see how Misty is doing." (Mal elbowed me.) "But right now," she went on, "we have a job to do."

I watched the faces of the other club members turn from happy and expectant to worried and uncertain.

Kristy organized the pile of papers before her into a neat stack. "Now," she said, "I've

118

made those special ballots, just like I said I would. Each piece of paper is headed with the name of one of the offices. Below that are the names of the four officers. All you have to do is make an X in the box by the name of the person you'd like to see in the office. Okay?"

The rest of us nodded our heads.

"Great," said Kristy. "Let's start with treasurer." She handed blank ballots to Mary Anne, Claudia, Mal, and me, and then gave one to herself.

"Everyone votes except Dawn," she reminded us.

Mary Anne raised her hand. "Uh, Kristy," she said timidly, "I'm — I'm really sorry, but I have to say something about that."

"Yeah?" replied Kristy.

"Well, it's just — it's just that, for instance, Dawn might not want to be the treasurer anymore, but maybe she's got a good idea about who the new treasurer should be. Who would know that better than Dawn? I understand what you said about ties, but I think we should *all* get to vote. If there's a tie, we'll have a revote. If we have to have too many revotes, then we'll think about letting only five people vote. But we should vote with six first."

I have to hand it to both Kristy and Mary

Anne. Kristy listened to Mary Anne's suggestion and took it seriously, and Mary Anne didn't cry.

"Okay," said Kristy, "let's vote on what Mary Anne said. Nothing fancy, just a show of hands. All those in favor of letting everyone vote in the elections, raise your hand."

Five hands went up. (Guess which one didn't?)

"Great. I guess we're all voting," said Kristy. "Luckily, I made extra ballots, in case of mistakes, so we're ready."

Kristy handed a ballot to Dawn. Then she gave each of us a blue ballpoint pen.

I looked at my ballot, my heart pounding. TREASURER was written across the top. Below it were the names Kristy, Claudia, Mary Anne, and Dawn. A box had been drawn to the left of each name.

I paused for a moment, but I knew what I was going to do. I picked up the pen and made an X next to Dawn's name. She was the best treasurer I could think of. But I was pretty sure she was going to kill me when she found out what I'd done (*if* she found out). The business of elections had started because the girls were tired of their old jobs and wanted a change. Well, too bad. I couldn't help that. Dawn was my choice for treasurer.

120

I glanced around Claudia's room and tried to measure the tension in the air. Funny, but there didn't seem to be much of it. The club members were busy voting, that was true, but more than that, no one was arguing. I think we were relieved that election day had finally come, no matter what it would bring.

When everyone had voted, we folded our papers in quarters and gave them back to Kristy, who carefully put them in a pile. Then she handed out the ballots for secretary, a few minutes later the ones for vice-president, and last of all, the ones for president. Each time, I voted quickly, knowing just what I had to do.

After the ballots for the office of president had been collected, Kristy said, "Let me just take a fast look through the ballots. If I see a lot of problems, I'll ask you guys to help me count."

Kristy picked up the ballots for treasurer and glanced at them.

"Hmm," she said.

She looked at the ballots for secretary.

"Huh," she said.

She looked at the ballots for vice-president.

"Well," she said,

And then she looked at the ballots for president.

She burst out laughing.

"What *is* it?" cried Claudia.

"You will not believe this," Kristy told us. "I hardly believe it myself."

"But?" Dawn prompted her.

"But we unanimously voted ourselves back into our old offices! We all voted for Dawn for treasurer — even Dawn did. We all voted for Mary Anne for secretary — even Mary Anne did. And so on. You guys even voted for me for president."

There was a moment of silence. Then every single one of us began to laugh. Dawn laughed so hard she cried. Kristy laughed so hard I thought she was going to fall out of the director's chair. And all the time we were laughing I was thinking. Now I understand what Mama meant when I asked her to tell me how to vote. She meant (but wanted me to figure out for myself) that we shouldn't worry about who thought what or who would be mad or who would laugh about our choices. The purpose of an election is to vote the best person into an office. Period. And we realized that. We realized that the best people were already *in* the offices and we wanted to keep them there.

The laughter was fading, and Kristy straightened up in her chair. "What happened?" she asked us.

I raised my hand, heart pounding. I usually

122

don't speak up much in meetings, but I was pretty sure I had the right answer this time. "I think," I began, "that we realized the best people had already been elected to the offices. I mean, Dawn is organized, but Mary Anne is even more organized, and Dawn is better at keeping figures straight, so Dawn's the perfect treasurer and Mary Anne's the perfect secretary. It would be tough to name anyone but Claudia as vice-president, and Kristy, you really deserve to be president since the club *was* your idea."

Everyone was looking at me and nodding. I added one more thing. "Can you live with the results of the election?" I asked the four officers. "You were pretty fed up with your jobs a little while ago."

"I can do it," said Dawn quickly, and the others agreed. "There are parts of my job that I don't like, but I guess I know I'm best at this job. And it would really mess up the club to start switching things around."

My friends were smiling again. Then Kristy's smile faded. "I have something to say," she began. "Okay, we realized we were in the right offices. But I have to admit that right office or not, I have been too bossy. Maybe I do come up with good ideas, but I shouldn't force them on you. It's — it's just this thing

123

with Charlie, I guess. You know something? I don't think he's acting like a big shot because he'll be in college. I think he's worried that he won't get into college, and he's taking his worries out by bossing me around. Then I take things out by bossing everyone else around. Jackie Rodowsky pointed that out to me. I mean, he pointed out that I was bossing him around. So I'm going to try to be better. No more forcing rules on you guys. When I get a new idea we'll vote on it, okay?"

"All *right!*" cried Claudia.

So the meeting ended happily. And when Kristy suggested again that we go over to the Mancusis', everyone wanted to see Misty. And Mal didn't mind. She was glad our club was a club again.

So was I.

CHAPTER 14

W̶e arrived at the Mancusis' just before twelve-thirty. Mr. and Mrs. Mancusi wouldn't be home until later in the afternoon.

I unlocked the front door, feeling like a nervous grandmother. How was Misty doing? Had she had her babies yet? How long did a hamster take to have babies anyway?

"Follow me," I said. "Misty's in the kitchen." (For some reason I was whispering.)

I tiptoed into the kitchen, and Mal, Kristy, Claudia, Dawn, and Mary Anne tiptoed after me. I paused in the doorway, listening for unusual sounds, although what sounds a baby hamster might make I cannot imagine.

At last I looked into Misty's cage. There she was, a golden brown body. . . . And there were four tiny pink bodies! They looked like jelly beans. They had no hair at all and their eyes were closed.

I gasped. "She's had them!" I whispered. "Misty had four babies!"

Everyone crowded around the cage.

"Make that five," said Kristy softly.

"Oh, EW!" exclaimed Mary Anne, backing away. "That is disgusting."

"No, it isn't. It's beautiful," said Dawn.

"Five babies. I wonder what the Mancusis will name them," said Mal. "I wonder if there will be more than five."

"*I* wonder if they'll keep them," said Claudia. "Do you think they will, Jessi?"

I shrugged. "I don't think another cageful of hamsters would be much extra work."

"Is there anything we're supposed to be doing for Misty or her babies?" asked Mary Anne, even though she wouldn't look in the cage anymore.

"I don't think so," I replied. "Doctor West said to be sure not to touch the babies, even if I think one is dead. He said Misty will know what to do. He said the babies — actually he called them pups — will get scattered all around the cage, but that Misty will take care of them."

We watched for a few more minutes. Finally I said, "Maybe we should leave Misty alone. If I were in a cage giving birth to hamsters, I wouldn't want six faces staring at me."

"If you were in a cage giving birth to ham-

126

sters," said Mal, "you'd be a miracle of science."

"No, she'd be in a zoo!" said Kristy.

We left the kitchen and wandered into the living room.

"Aw," said Claudia, "who's this guy?"

"That's Powder. Hey, do you want to meet the rest of the Mancusis' animals? I mean, do all of you want to meet them?"

"Thanks, but I've already met Barney," Mary Anne replied drily.

"There are other animals here, though, and Kristy and Dawn haven't been over before. Also — "

"Where's the beef? Where's the beef?"

"Aughh!" shrieked Kristy. "Someone's in the house! We're not alone!"

Dawn began to laugh. "It's a bird, isn't it?"

I nodded.

"We used to have one," Dawn told us. "A long time ago. I think it was a parakeet. His name was Buzz. He could say a few words. But the funniest thing he ever did was fly into a bowl of mashed potatoes."

"Dawn!" I exclaimed. "Is that true?"

"Cross my heart," she replied.

It must have been true.

We were all laughing hysterically and couldn't calm down for awhile. When we finally did,

127

we checked on Misty (six babies) and then I let Kristy and Dawn meet the animals.

"Hey, Mary Anne!" called Kristy as we were leaving the sun porch. "Where's the lid to Barney's cage?"

Mary Anne began screaming without even turning around to look at the cage. If she had turned around, she would have seen that the lid was on tightly. Kristy had to confess her joke in order to keep Mary Anne from running home.

At last I suggested that we take Cheryl, Jacques, and Pooh Bear on their afternoon walk. I thought my friends might enjoy that.

So we took the dogs on a long walk. When we returned I said, "Well, you guys, I hate to kick you out, but I have to feed the animals. And I should probably be the only one here when the Mancusis come home."

"Okay," Kristy answered. "We understand."

My friends left. I was alone in the house, although not for long. The Mancusis would return soon. Even so, I phoned my parents to tell them where I was and why I'd be late. Then I looked in on Misty. *Ten* pups! And they were all gathered around their mother in a big jumbly pile of legs and feet and ears. I guess

Misty had finished giving birth. Now she could tend to her babies.

While I waited for the Mancusis, I found a roll of crepe paper (out in the garage, with all the boxes) and tied a big red bow to each of the dogs' collars.

"You three look lovely," I told them. "You're doggie fashion plates."

"Rowf?" asked Jacques, cocking his head.

"Yes, you're very handsome."

I was about to make bows for the cats when I heard a car pull into the driveway. "Guess who's home!" I called to the dogs.

Of course, they had no idea, but when I ran to the front door, they followed me. I opened the inside door and waved to Mr. and Mrs. Mancusi as they unloaded their luggage from the car. They were surprised to see me, but they smiled and waved back. Then, their arms weighed down with suitcases, they walked to the front door, while I tried to open it for them and hold the dogs back at the same time. It wasn't easy, but we managed.

As soon as the Mancusis were safely inside, I cried, "Guess what! One of the hamsters had babies! . . . Oh, I hope you had a nice vacation."

"My heavens!" exclaimed Mrs. Mancusi.

"One of the hamsters had babies?! How could we have missed a pregnancy? Are the babies okay? Which hamster is it?"

"Everything's fine. Honest," I told them. "I knew something was wrong, well, I knew something was *unusual*, so my mom drove the hamster and me to your vet yesterday. Dr. West looked at her and he told me what to do."

"Oh. . . ." The Mancusis let out a sigh of relief.

"Do you want to see the babies?" I asked.

"Of course," said Mr. Mancusi. He and his wife put down their suitcases and followed me into the kitchen, the dogs bounding joyfully at our sides.

"It's this one," I said. "I moved the other hamsters to the aquarium on the table." I stood back so the Mancusis could look in at Misty.

"Ah, Snicklefritz." Mrs. Mancusi scratched her head. "How did we miss this? I really apologize, Jessi. But I have to congratulate you. You did a terrific job in a difficult situation. We're very grateful to you."

"I guess," added Mr. Mancusi, "that in the excitement when we were trying to get away — our pet-sitter canceling and all — we just didn't notice that Snicklefritz was pregnant."

"Well, everything worked out fine," I spoke

up. "Mis — I mean, Snicklefritz has ten babies."

The Mancusis watched them for a few moments. Then they turned to me. "Thank you again, Jessi," said Mr. Mancusi. "You've been very responsible." He handed me some money — much more than I've gotten paid for any other job.

"Wow!" I cried. "Thanks. . . . Are you sure this isn't too much?"

"Not at all."

"By the way," said Mrs. Mancusi, "do you have any friends who would like a hamster? We'll let the babies go to anyone who will give them good homes — in about three weeks, that is. After the pups are weaned."

"*Any*one?" I repeated. "Gosh, we've never had a pet. I'm sure my sister Becca would like one. *I'd* like one. And, well, I'll spread the word. I bet I can help you find lots of homes!"

I couldn't believe it. A pet! Would Mama and Daddy let us have one? I had no idea. Neither Becca nor I had ever asked for a pet.

I headed for the front door. The dogs followed me.

"Good-bye, Cheryl. Good-bye, Jacques. Good-bye, Pooh Bear," I said.

The Mancusis were right behind the dogs. "They really like you," Mr. Mancusi said. "Oh, and *we* like their bows. Very spiffy."

I smiled. "Well, thanks again. If you ever need another pet-sitter, let me know. And I'll find out about homes for the baby hamsters. I promise."

The Mancusis and I called good-bye to each other and then I ran to my house. I was just about bursting with my news — Snicklefritz's babies and homes for them. Maybe one would become our first pet.

"Mama! Daddy!" I shouted as I burst through our front door.

The Braddocks were back. Ballet school was in session again. My life had returned to normal.

I missed the Mancusi animals, but I could probably visit them any time I wanted to. I'm sure I'd be allowed to walk the dogs from time to time.

Anyway, since my life was back to normal, I baby-sat for the Braddocks the next day, Monday, and then tore over to Claudia's house. I reached it a full five minutes before the meeting was supposed to start. I even beat Kristy, but of course she's at the mercy of Charlie, so she doesn't have a lot of control over when she arrives.

Claudia and Dawn were there, though.

"Hi, you guys!" I said as I entered Claud's room.

"Hello," they replied, smiling, and Dawn added, "You sound awfully happy."

"Glad to be back at the Braddocks'?" asked Claudia.

"Yes," I answered, "but it's more than that. I'll tell you all about it when everybody's here."

"Okay," said Claud. "Potato chips, anyone?"

"Oh, I'm starving!" I exclaimed, even though I sort of watch my diet because I have to stay in good shape for dance class.

"Um, can you help me find them?" asked Claud, looking puzzled. "They might be under the bed, but who knows?"

Claudia and Dawn and I dropped to our stomachs and crawled halfway under Claud's bed. A ton of junk had been stashed there — boxes of art supplies, folders of drawings and sketches, magazines for making collages, that sort of thing. And because Claudia is such a poor speller, they were labeled SKECHES or PANTINGS or BURSHES.

I found the potato chips in a box marked CALAGE SUPPLIES.

"Here they are!" I announced.

The three of us crawled out from under the bed, stood up, turned around, and found Kristy, Mallory, and Mary Anne staring at us. We began to laugh — all six of us.

"That was so attractive!" said Kristy. "I hope

134

I always come to a meeting just in time to see the three of you backing out from under a bed."

"My backside is my best side," replied Dawn, looking serious.

There was more laughter as the members of the Baby-sitters Club settled into their usual places. Kristy climbed into the director's chair. She put her visor on. She stuck a pencil over one ear.

And then she pulled a new checklist out of her pocket, smoothed the creases, and with big, showy sweeps of her arms, tacked it up on the bulletin board over the photos of Claudia and Stacey.

"There," she said with satisfaction.

Claudia, Mary Anne, Dawn, Mallory, and I just stared at her. I guess my mouth was hanging open. Everybody else's was.

"I don't believe it," muttered Claudia, but just when it looked like she might jump to her feet and strangle Kristy, Kristy jumped to *her* feet and ripped the checklist off the bulletin board.

"Now watch this, everyone," she announced. She scrunched up the checklist and threw it in the wastebasket. "'Bye-bye, checklist. That's the last of it. You won't see it or hear about it again."

At first the rest of us didn't know what to do. Then we began to smile.

"You mean that was a joke?" exclaimed Claudia. "Oh, my lord! *Kristy . . . "*

Kristy grinned at us. She looked like the Cheshire Cat reclining in his tree.

Dawn threw a potato chip at her. I think a potato chip war might have started if the phone hadn't rung.

"Oh, no! We haven't done any of our opening business!" cried Kristy. "Dawn hasn't collected dues, I haven't — "

Ring, ring.

Kristy stopped ranting and raving and answered the phone. "Hello, Baby-sitters Club."

We arranged a Saturday afternoon job for me with the Arnold twins. Then Kristy got down to business.

"Dawn?" she said. "Ms. Treasurer?"

"I need your dues," announced Dawn.

Dawn collected the dues while we groaned and complained. "I'll walk out with you after the meeting and pay Charlie," she told Kristy.

"Okay. Thanks. That'll be fine. Maybe that will improve Charlie's mood." Kristy paused. "All right," she continued, "any club business?"

"I have something to ask everyone," I said,

"but it can wait until after the real club business is over."

Kristy nodded. "Anything else?"

The rest of the girls shook their heads.

"Okay," said Kristy. "I'm done. Over to you, Jessi. Oh, by the way, did you all notice that I didn't ask whether you'd read the notebook?"

"Uh, yes," replied Dawn.

"Good. I'm not going to ask anymore. I'll trust you to read it. No questions, no checklists — "

"You'll actually trust us?" exclaimed Mary Anne.

"I'll actually trust you."

The phone rang again, and we arranged another job. When that was taken care of, I said, "Well, guess what. Misty's name turns out to be Snicklefritz and she had *ten* pups yesterday." (Mallory knew this already, since we tell each other everything. But the others hadn't heard.)

"Ten pups!" cried Mary Anne. "What will the Mancusis do with them?"

"Well, that's the rest of my news. The Mancusis are giving them away — to anyone who'll promise the babies a good home. *And* Mama and Daddy said Becca and I can have one! Our first pet! We decided to name our hamster Misty no matter what color it is, and whether it's a boy or a girl."

"Oh, that's great!" cried Mary Anne and Kristy at the same time. (They both have pets.)

"And," I went on, "I'm asking around, finding out if anyone else would like a hamster. How about one of you?"

Claudia shook her head. "They're cute, but I hate cleaning cages."

Mary Anne shook her head. "A hamster wouldn't last a second around Tigger."

Kristy shook her head. "We've got enough pets at our house already."

Dawn shook her head. "I like hamsters, but if I get a pet, I'd like a bigger one. A cat or a dog."

I looked at Mallory. She seemed thoughtful. "We've got ten people in our family," she said slowly, "but no pets. I don't see why we couldn't get one little pet. The younger kids would like a hamster. So would the boys. Well, so would all of us." Mallory dove for the phone. "Mom! Mom!" she cried.

(I could just imagine Mrs. Pike saying, "What on earth is the matter?")

"Mom, the Mancusis are going to give the hamster babies away. In about three weeks, I think." (I nodded.) "Could we have one? It

138

would be a good experience for Claire and Margo. And I think Nicky would like a pet . . . Yeah? . . . I know . . . Okay . . . Okay, thanks! This is great! 'Bye, Mom." Mallory hung up. "We can have one!" she announced. "We'll be getting our first pet, too!"

I have never seen so much excitement.

Then the phone rang and we lined up three jobs.

When the phone rang a fourth time, Mary Anne opened the record book again, and we sat up eagerly. I picked up the receiver. "Hello, Baby-sitters Club," I said.

"Hi," answered a very small voice. "I —This is Jackie Rodowsky. Is Kristy there, please?"

"Sure, Jackie. Hold on," I told him.

I handed the phone to Kristy, whispering, "It's Jackie Rodowsky."

Kristy raised her eyebrows. "Hi, Jackie."

That was all she said, and Jackie burst into tears.

"What's wrong?" she asked him. "What happened? Is your mom home?"

"She's here," Jackie told her. "And I'm okay. I mean, I'm not hurt. But we had our class elections today."

"Oh," said Kristy. "Right. And what happened?"

"I lost. Adrienne beat me. I tried and tried

to show the kids that I could take care of Snowball. But I don't think they believed me." Jackie paused. When he started speaking again, his voice was trembling. "I just — just wanted a pet to take care of by myself. That's all."

"Jackie," said Kristy gently, "I'm sorry you lost. I'm sorry the kids wouldn't pay attention to you. Really I am. Sometimes things just work out that way. But listen, could I talk to your mom for a sec, please?" There was a pause while Kristy waited for Mrs. Rodowsky to get on the phone. Then she said, "Hi, Mrs. Rodowsky. This is Kristy Thomas. Jackie told me about the elections today and I was wondering — could he have a pet of his own? I think he wants one, and I know where he could get a free hamster. . . . Yes. . . . Really? Oh, terrific! Could I talk to Jackie again, please?"

So Kristy gave Jackie the good news about his hamster.

"My own? My own hamster?" Jackie shrieked. "Amazing! What will I name it? Is it a boy or a girl? What color is it?"

Kristy couldn't answer his questions, so we arranged for me to take him over to the Mancusis' in a couple of weeks. The hamsters wouldn't be ready to leave their mother yet, but Jackie could look at them and pet them and play with them in order to choose the one

140

that would become his very own. Jackie liked the idea a lot. So he thanked Kristy eleven times and then they got off the phone.

"Well, all's well that ends well," said Kristy.

"Huh?" said Claudia.

"I mean, happy endings everywhere you look. We got our club problems straightened out. The sick hamster turned out to be pregnant, and then she had her babies and they were born without any trouble, and now Jessi and Mallory's families will have their first pets, and Jackie lost the election but he got a hamster. Happy endings."

"Yeah," I said, smiling.

The numbers on Claudia's digital clock turned from 5:59 to 6:00.

"Meeting adjourned," announced our president.

I walked out with Mal. "I wonder," I said, "if I could talk Becca into changing Misty's name to Mancusi."

"Darn!" said Mallory. "That's what I wanted to name our hamster."

"Really?"

"Nah."

We giggled.

"Call you tonight!" I shouted to Mal as we separated.

Best friends have to talk a lot.

About the Author

ANN M. MARTIN did *a lot* of baby-sitting when she was growing up in Princeton, New Jersey. Now her favorite baby-sitting charge is her cat, Mouse, who lives with her in her Manhattan apartment.

Ann Martin's Apple Paperbacks are *Bummer Summer, Inside Out, Stage Fright, Me and Katie (the Pest)*, and all the other books in the Baby-sitters Club series.

She is a former editor of books for children, and was graduated from Smith College. She likes ice cream, the beach, and *I Love Lucy*; and she hates to cook.